029487

ROYAL AGRICULTURAL COLLEGE

CROP PROTECTION
IN THE DEVELOPING WORLD

BCPC Monograph No 61

D0530665

ROYAL A

CROP PROTECTION IN THE DEVELOPING WORLD

BCPC Monograph No 61

Proceedings of an international
symposium organised by
the BRITISH CROP PROTECTION COUNCIL
and held at the Brighton Metropole Hotel
on 21 November 1994

Edited by Robert Black and Anne Sweetmore

BCPC Registered Office:
49 Downing Street
Farnham
Surrey GU9 7PH, UK.

© 1994 The British Crop Protection Council
49 Downing Street
Farnham, Surrey GU9 7PH

All rights reserved. No part of this publication may be
reproduced, stored in a retrieval system, or transmitted, in
any form or by any means, electronic, mechanical,
photocopying, recording or otherwise, without the prior
permission of the copyright owner.

British Library Cataloguing in Publication Data.
A catalogue record for this book is available from the British Library

British Crop Protection Council
Crop Protection in the Developing World
(Monograph Series, ISSN 0306-3941; No 61)

ISBN 0 948404 84 1

Cover design by Major Design & Production Ltd, Nottingham
Printed in Great Britain by Major Print Ltd, Nottingham

CONTENTS

PREFACE

With increasing pressure on land in the developing world, any additional production must come from improved yields. Crop protection has a crucial role to play in increasing production. However, overall performance is unlikely to be satisfactory unless the supporting institutions — the *software of development* — are greatly improved.

Additional production is necessary to satisfy the needs of a growing population, many of whom are in urban areas where they are food consumers. Also, rural populations are increasingly forced to compete for scarce resources such as land and water. The task of achieving a boost in crop yield is urgent because extreme poverty and low productivity still characterise many low-income economies. If the yield-increasing strategy fails to work, then food prices will rise or import bills will climb, and inevitably the poorest groups will suffer. In low-income situations the poorest buy food and therefore it is likely that the single best measure to affect their welfare is to keep the prices of basic food items down. To keep prices down we have to increase supply.

It is now a commonplace to argue that to increase crop (and livestock) yields most effectively and efficiently we need simultaneously to apply a package of inputs. The corollary is less commonly recognised: much of the investment in one input can be wasted if another part of the package is missing. For example, there is little point in pumping water to irrigate if the crop is to be eaten by locusts, or if the seed is of poor genetic stock and will lodge when yield-inducing inputs are applied.

Investment in a set of complementary inputs is more likely to be undertaken by low-income farmers if the risk of loss is reduced. Thus the benefits from successful crop protection will be seen not only directly in reduced pest damage, but in an indirect way by encouraging investment in items such as irrigation, fertiliser, the best seeds, and regular labour inputs for weeding.

Reducing the variance of a rising average crop yield can be as important as increasing the average. It was demonstrated many years ago in India that irrigation investment, whilst increasing average yields, could actually increase the level of yield variation from year to year and not, as we might expect, lower the variance in yields. This strange effect occurs because of irregularities in the supply of other yield-enhancing inputs, particularly fertiliser.

Theodore Schultz, the Nobel Prize-winning agricultural economist, demonstrated 30 years ago that there was very little scope for achieving any increases in production by rearranging the way low-income farmers went about their work. They were *efficient but poor*, and to release them from their poverty trap, new technologies were needed.

Today we have new technologies available, but for their adoption there is a need for finance to be extended to small-scale farmers, in order to enable them to acquire these inputs. Unfortunately, credit schemes for the small-scale farmer have rarely been successful.

More generally, most of the traditional institutions that would need to improve in order to support the adoption of agricultural technology, including education, extension, management, tenure rules, and law and order, might also be described as being, in the Schultzian sense, unimprovable without the injection of new resources.

Experience suggests that improvement in these institutions, however indispensable, will be difficult and slow to achieve and transformation is unlikely in the near term. The technology that might help stimulate institutional reform is lagging behind the scientific advances that agronomists are helping to create.

Several of the nine papers in this monograph tackle various technological aspects of crop protection but recognise the critical importance of understanding farm-level constraints of a technical, economic and social nature, and of developing policies that build on this insight. They call for greater recognition and effort in applying policies by improving resource management at all levels. They demonstrate a recognition that widespread use of both new and traditional technologies is an integral part of the struggle to grow adequate quantities of food close to the consumers, and to grow it efficiently, so as to remove some of the widespread problems of rural poverty.

The papers in this volume should stimulate debate on many of the important issues facing crop protection in the developing world. The monograph opens with introductory papers on the realities of crop protection in Zanzibar (Marshed-Kharusy) and on more wide-ranging policy questions (Mumford & Stonehouse). The debate on subsistence farming *versus* cash cropping is mirrored in discussions of appropriate technology (Smith; Croxton, for instance). Calls for simplified analytical procedures for pesticides and for sympathetically geared pesticide training are made (Cox; Ledru, Thomas & Prétot), while Legge provides assurances that we do not need to fear contamination of our imported food with pesticides. Further insight into the kind of technology that could be adopted is provided by Banpot Napompeth and by Hilder & Hamilton.

Ian Carruthers
Symposium Chairman
Wye College
September 1994

ABBREVIATIONS

acid equivalent	a.e.	nuclear magnetic resonance	nmr
active ingredient	AI	number average diameter	n.a.d.
boiling point	b.p.	number median diameter	n.m.d.
British Standards Institution	BSI	organic matter	o.m.
centimetre(s)	cm	page	p.
concentration x time product	ct	pages	pp.
concentration required to kill		parts per million by volume	mg/l
50% of test organisms	LC50	parts per million by weight	mg/kg
correlation coefficient	r	pascal	Pa
cultivar	cv.	percentage	%
cultivars	cvs.	post-emergence	post-em.
day(s)	d	power take off	p.t.o.
days after treatment	DAT	pre-emergence	pre-em.
degrees Celsius (centigrade)	°C	probability (statistical)	P
dose required to kill 50% of		relative humidity	r.h.
test organisums	LD50	revolutions per minute	rev./min
dry matter	d.m.	second (time unit)	s
Edition	Edn	standard error	SE
Editor	Ed	standard error of means	SEM
Editors	Eds	soluble powder	SP
emulsifiable concentrate	EC	species (singular)	sp.
freezing point	f.p.	species (plural)	spp.
gas chromatography-mass		square metre	m^2
spectrometry	gcms	subspecies	ssp.
gas-liquid chromatography	glc	surface mean diameter	s.m.d.
gram(s)	g	suspension concentrate	SC
growth stage	GS	temperature	temp.
hectare(s)	ha	thin-layer chromatography	tlc
high performance (or pressure)		tonne(s)	t
liquid chromatography	hplc	ultraviolet	u.v.
hour	h	vapour pressure	v.p.
infrared	i.r.	variety (wild plant use)	var.
International Standardisation		volume	V
Organisation	ISO	weight	W
Kelvin	K	weight by volume	W/V
kilogram(s)	kg	(mass by volume is more correct)	(m/V)
least significant difference	LSD	weight by weight	W/W
litre(s)	Litre	(mass by mass is more correct)	(m/m)
litres per hectare	l/ha	wettable powder	WP
mass	m		
mass per mass	m/m	approximately	c.
mass per volume	m/V	less than	<
mass spectrometry	m.s.	more than	>
maximum	max.	not less than	≮
melting point	m.p.	not more than	>
metre(s)	m	Multiplying symbols-	Prefixes
milligram(s)	mg	mega (x 10^6)	M
millilitre(s)	ml	kilo (x 10^3)	k
millimetre(s)	mm	milli (x 10^{-3})	m
minimum	min.	micro (x 10^{-6})	μ
minute (time unit)	min	nano (x 10^{-9})	n
molar concentration	M	pico (x 10^{-12})	p

Session 1
Introduction

PLANT PROTECTION IN THE DEVELOPING WORLD: PROBLEMS AND NEEDS. LESSONS FROM ZANZIBAR

M.N. MARSHED-KHARUSY

Plant Protection Division, Ministry of Agriculture, Livestock and Natural Resources, P.O. Box 1062, Zanzibar, Tanzania

ABSTRACT

Zanzibar is an example of a less-developed country facing a number of issues that affect plant protection. These are the pests and diseases themselves, problems at the farmer level (such as lack of cash, land tenure), traditional resistance to new approaches in plant protection, weak institutions including the quarantine services, and problems of policy formulation. Measures to be taken in order to improve the situation include developing and devising crop protection strategies based on farmers' needs, strengthening institutions, and developing sound policies.

INTRODUCTION

Zanzibar, which is part of Tanzania, consists of two major islands, Unguja and Pemba, and a number of small, sparsely populated islands. The two major islands have an area of 1658 and 985 km², respectively. They lie between 4° and 6° south, 39° east, 40 km (Unguja) and 60 km (Pemba) off the coast of mainland Tanzania. The climate is warm (mean annual temperature of 27°C) and humid (mean humidity of 76-78%), with four seasons, each about 3 months. The average annual rainfall is higher in Pemba (1800 mm) than Unguja (1400 mm). The islands are inhabited by about 800,000 people.

The economy of Zanzibar depends largely on agriculture, which contributes over 70% of the gross domestic product (GDP). More than 90% of the total foreign exchange earnings come from this sector. About 80% of the population depend on agriculture, either directly or indirectly (Wirth *et al.*, 1988). Taking Zanzibar as an example of a less-developed country with limited resources and few qualified personnel, several problems are encountered in developing plant protection strategies. These are both technical and institutional, while sometimes even political interference results in poor execution of recommended activities. Some of the problems encountered are discussed below.

The Agriculture and Livestock policy of 1984 (Ministry of Agriculture and Livestock Development, 1984) states that "The Zanzibar economy will continue to depend on clove industry for many years to come". It is true that Zanzibar still depends on cloves, but low demand for the crop and poor prices have crippled the economy of the islands (Robbins, 1987). However food imports (rice, wheat flour, sugar) have been steadily increasing (FAO/IFAD, 1987). Therefore the government of Zanzibar has had to shift its emphasis from the development of government parastatals and cooperative farms towards encouraging small-holder production. Measures are being taken to diversify the clove-dependent economy by introducing other cash crops, and to promote tourism.

The farming area is mainly divided into three ecological zones, the plantation area (high rainfall) with tree crops like cloves, coconuts and other food crops; coral rag area (low rainfall) with crops like maize, sorghum and pigeon pea; and lowland (valleys) mainly growing rice. In Zanzibar, as in many developing countries, agriculture is at the subsistence level. Farmers own small plots of 0.5-3 hectares. With the exception of few crops like rice, most crops are intercropped, with mixed farming.

PROBLEMS IN PLANT PROTECTION

Pests and diseases

Zanzibar is a typical tropical island with a warm and humid climate which is much favoured by pests and plant pathogens. At any time of the year, different crops can be found in the field, and therefore hosts are present continuously. A typical example is that of the rice hispa beetle (*Trichispa* spp). This beetle was not a pest of any significance a few years ago, but soon after the development of irrigation in the rice valleys in Pemba, farmers started cultivating two crops per year. Within five years, hispa has become a serious pest causing extensive problems in rice, both directly as a damaging pest, and as a vector of rice yellow mottle virus.

Several other pests cause serious damage, although no thorough yield-loss assessment has been carried out on any crop. Usually it is the farmers who sound the alarm before any action is taken. From the farming systems studies carried out by the Zanzibar Cash Crops Farming Systems Project (ZCCFSP) and the Plant Protection Division (PPD), the major pests and diseases identified are shown in Table 1.

Problems at the farmer level

Farming in Zanzibar is typically subsistence, with little produce left over for sale, hence farmers lack cash to buy inputs or hire labour for farming activities (Wirth *et al.*, 1988). Credit facilities are not available to them. Production is low due to low inputs, poor soil fertility, poor agricultural practices and lack of access to information on good farming practices.

When there is any outbreak of pests and diseases, farmers become alarmed because their means of survival is threatened. The knowledge that pesticides may be made available by the government free of charge has made farmers reluctant to take any action at an early stage, and has encouraged dependence on the extension service as the provider of pesticides rather than advice on pest management.

Land ownership has also been a serious handicap to the practice of any long-term preventative or control measures. In theory the government owns all the land. This is especially important on rice lands, where the government insists on rice cultivation being maintained. Without ownership rights to the land, the farmer cannot invest in improved soil fertility measures or practise control measures such as fallow, crop rotation etc., for fear of losing that piece of land.

TABLE 1. Major pests and diseases of principal crops in Zanzibar.

Crop	Major problem and causal organism	Extent of damage and control
Cash crops		
Cloves	Sudden death disease Mycoplasma-like organisms (MLOs)	Can kill trees rapidly within a short period. No effective control measures at present (Campbell, 1940; Dabek *et al.*, 1985; Martin, 1989).
	Acute dieback (fungal disease) *Cryphonectria cubensis*	A disease related to physical damage. Almost all trees are infected. Pruning has not been an effective control measure (Martin, 1989).
	Termites *Macrotermes subhyalimus*	Becoming serious even to other tree and forest crops (Martin, 1989; Marshed *et al.*, 1993).
Coconuts	Rhinocerous beetle *Oryctes monocerous*	Serious to dwarf cultivars. Biological control tried but not successful for small-scale farmers (Van Huis, 1991).
	Coconut bug *Pseudotheraptus wayi*	Very serious, may cause up to 100% losses. Biological control by *Oecophylla longinoda* shows more potential than chemical control (Way, 1953; Brown, 1955; Oswald, 1985, 1988).
	Wilting disorder (cause unknown)	Yellowing and eventual death of the plant. Association with pathogens not confirmed (Black, 1991).
Food crops		
Rice	Black beetle *Heteronychus* spp	Serious on localised rainfed areas. Losses up to 100%. Research in progress (Van der Weel, 1992; Marshed, 1993a).
	Rice hispa beetle *Trichispa sericea* and rice yellow mottle virus	Serious in irrigated rice in Pemba island. IPM is now being tested (Van Keulen *et al.*, 1993).
	Armyworm *Spodoptera exempta*	Sporadic but can be very serious. Mainly on rice. Chemical control available but not economical.
	Edible grasshopper *Homorocoryhus nitidulus*	Sporadic but serious to rice, millet and sorghum. No effective control measures (Marshed, 1993b).
Cassava	Cassava mealybug *Phenococcus manihoti*	Serious when first introduced to Zanzibar. Biological control has been more effective on Unguja than Pemba island.
	Cassava mosaic virus and green spider mite *Mononychellus tanajoa*	Very serious. Losses up to 90%. No effective control measures (Begg & Makame, 1983).
Banana	Black Sigatoka *Mycosphaerella fijiensis*	Very serious. No loss assessment done but drastic national decline in production.
Cowpeas	Aphids Pod borers and others	Serious. No loss assessment. Research in progress.
Maize	Stem borers	Losses up to 30%. Chemical control available but not suitable (van Keulen, 1990).

Approaches in plant protection

For many years the Ministry of Agriculture imported pesticides with little knowledge of their uses. Due to lack of qualified staff, recommendations were made in a haphazard manner, without proper evaluation of the problem. The solution to any pest or disease problem was considered to be pesticide application. Furthermore, it was the Ministry's responsibility to provide farmers with sprayers and workers to do the spraying. The pesticides were sold at a subsidised rate, or sometimes given free of charge, hence farmers could apply any amount they wished to.

More recently, with the inception of a number of agricultural development projects, including a Dutch project to strengthen the Plant Protection Division of Zanzibar, this approach is gradually changing. Farmers now have access to diagnostic services, research and extension, and the concept of integrated pest management (IPM) has been introduced. However, there are initial problems, such as poor collaboration (research and extension are discipline-oriented), conventional approaches to research (researchers and extensionists dictate the programmes) and inadequate coordination of activities.

Although there are no restrictions on the importation of pesticides by external agencies, very few of them do so because they cannot compete with the subsidised pesticides provided by the government. Also, it must be noted that in Zanzibar there is no legislation governing the importation, distribution and use of pesticides. (This is not so for the rest of the East African countries.)

Only the PPD and a few donor-funded projects can afford to provide protective gear to their workers, and generally no safety procedures are carried out by farmers. After the application of pesticides, the remainder is poured into river and stream water when cleaning the equipment. The same water is used by farmers for domestic purposes including bathing.

Institutional weaknesses

There is a shortage of qualified specialist staff to carry out coordinated research and extension activities. Funds for higher level training mainly depend on foreign donors. There is also little access to outside information from journals and bulletins due to a lack of local funds and external contacts. Up-to-date information is only available through the donor-funded projects, and when the donor leaves no further funding is provided by the government. Many less-developed countries have not yet ranked plant protection problems in terms of priorities, so that the limited resources available may be used on unnecessary research and other activities.

Quarantine threats

A lack of facilities for producing disease-free planting material also hampers the development of proper control measures. Therefore, there is pressure to use exotic planting material. The Zanzibar islands have a number of unofficial entry points and people can bring any plant material into the country without being noticed. There are no boats patrolling the coast of the islands, and therefore a number of inhabitants move between the islands, the Tanzania mainland and Kenya by canoes and dhows, and bring in planting materials illegally. Cassava mealybug, which entered the country on planting material, was introduced in this way. The pest was identified when it had already spread to many parts of the island and caused extensive damage. It has now become an established pest.

Politicians, scientists and influential businessmen have also been involved in bringing infected plant materials into the country in good faith, with the intention of helping farmers but with detrimental consequences, as these materials do not go through the local quarantine procedures.

Due to several weaknesses of quarantine in Zanzibar, the country is threatened by many pests and diseases from outside. Pests like the larger grain borer *Prostephanus truncatus* (Horn), and lethal yellowing of coconuts, are present in the Tanzania mainland and could be introduced into the islands. Pests and diseases of rice, legumes and root and tuber crops from South-East Asia and West Africa are also likely to be introduced, as well as pests and diseases of the proposed new cash crops for Zanzibar from different parts of the world, if proper quarantine measures are not followed.

Policy issues

Zanzibar's first agricultural policy was developed in 1984 and took almost three years to receive final approval (Ministry of Agriculture and Livestock Development, Zanzibar, 1984). Most of those who formulated the policy had little experience and hence quite a number of issues were omitted, for example the environmental hazards due to the importation of large quantities of pesticides. The policy was also overambitious and a number of goals could not be realised before its revision in 1991 (Ministry of Agriculture and Livestock Development, 1991).

No consideration was given to the government's financial ability to implement the activities listed in the policy. The question of sustainability of different projects, notably plant protection, was not discussed. Usually the budget allocation from the government for plant protection activities is very small; a large part of the funding comes from donors. When donor funds terminate, most of the activities will stop as well.

The plant protection legislation of 1939 (revised in 1965) which is now in use is old and outdated, and many developments have taken place since then. For example, no consideration is given to issues such as tissue culture and the importation of biological control agents.

CURRENT NEEDS IN PLANT PROTECTION

Based on the above-mentioned problems, there is a need to try to rectify the situation at different levels, as indicated below.

Needs at farmer level

● Formal and informal adult education to enable farmers to read and write, and thus improve the farmers' understanding of extension messages on different aspects of crop husbandry.

● Use of a participatory farming systems approach in problem identification and solution. This will create mutual understanding between researchers, extensionists and farmers.

There will be judicial use of the available resources and the research outcome will be acceptable to farmers.

- Implementation of the principles of IPM at farmer level. This includes training farmers in recognising and quantifying pests, diseases and natural enemies, so they can take their own appropriate pest management measures. The IPM approach is economic, sustainable and appropriate for subsistence farming.

- Provision of credit to farmers, giving them the opportunity to implement plant protection recommendations in the correct way. This will also help the government to implement a policy of removing subsidies and ceasing to provide free services, as it has been clearly shown that the government can no longer afford to do so. Removing all subsidies on pesticides is a first necessary step.

Strengthening of institutions

- Setting priorities for researchers, based on the level and importance of particular problems.

- Training of local staff at different levels according to need is one of the important factors when considering the question of sustainability of any programme. Although different donor-funded projects have trained a substantial number of local staff at Diploma, BSc and MSc levels, further training is still required at higher levels even to PhD in order to have more specialised staff. This is in accordance with government policy.

- Technical advice and short consultancies on specific issues such as IPM are required. The emphasis should be on exchange of ideas to enable local staff to gain experience and to execute activities independently.

- Easier contact with external institutions will provide local institutions with access to useful information concerning plant protection. It is necessary to take advantage of recent developments in information technology.

- Improving the operation of plant quarantine services (together with necessary policy support).

- An interdisciplinary approach in solving plant protection problems is cheaper, more economic and effective.

Development of sound policy

- The plant protection organisation must have a clearly defined policy and objectives. This policy should be able to influence the national policy whenever appropriate. Development projects must be in a position to advise on policy amendment whenever necessary.

- Plant protection legislation must be updated in conformity with existing technological developments.

- Advisory and coordinating bodies should be established to deal with matters concerning plant protection.

CONCLUSIONS

In order to provide sustainable and effective plant protection services, it is necessary to train both farmers and local staff, to follow an IPM approach, and to have sufficient local funds available to run day-to-day activities by providing credit to farmers.

There are no ready-made IPM packages for Zanzibar and other less-developed countries, and the use of high-input agriculture is not suitable. This poses a real challenge to local scientists to develop appropriate IPM packages that are in accordance with the existing farming systems.

In pursuing appropriate technologies for less-developed countries the question arises whether efforts should be concentrated on low-input agriculture, or on high-production agriculture sustained by considerable external inputs. Pulling subsistence farmers into a market economy is a major task in itself.

ACKNOWLEDGEMENTS

I am very thankful to the British Crop Protection Council for funding my participation in this symposium. Special thanks go to Ms Fadhila H. Ali of the Irrigation Project Zanzibar for her invaluable support, and Mr Ahmed M. Suleiman, Plant Protection Division, Dr Gerard Bruin and Ms Alida Laurense of the Project "Strengthening Plant Protection Division of Zanzibar" for their constructive suggestions.

REFERENCES

Begg, C.; Makame M. (1983) *Cassava Production in Zanzibar*. Ministry of Agriculture and Livestock Development, Zanzibar.

Black, R. (1991) *Further Investigation of Wilt Disorder of Coconut at Selem, Zanzibar*. Report of an NRI consultancy for Tanzania National Coconut Development Programme.

Brown, T.S. (1955) *Pseudotheraptus wayi* a new genus and species of Coreid (Hemiptera) injurious to coconuts in East Africa. *Bulletin of Entomological Research* **46**, 221-240.

Campbell, A.H. (1940) *Loss of Clove Trees through Sudden Death*. Zanzibar Government Report.

Dabek, A.J.; Jones, P.; Martin, P.J. (1985) Mycoplasma-like organism in clove trees affected by sudden death in Zanibar and Pemba. *Phytopathologische Zeitschrift* **104**, 180-184.

FAO/IFAD (1987) *United Republic of Tanzania, Zanzibar General Identification Mission*. Report of the Cooperation Programme of the Food and Agricultural Organization/International Fund for Agricultural Development.

Marshed, M.N. (1993a) Determination of the effective and economic dose of Miral-10G (Isozofos) to control Heteronychus beetle (Coleoptera:Dynastinae) in rainfed rice at Kibokwa Zanzibar. Report, Annual Zanzibar Agricultural Research Council review meeting, 17-18 May 1994 Zanzibar.

Marshed, M.N. (1993b) Problem of long horned grasshopper (edible grasshopper), *Homorocoryphus nitidulis* (Orthoptera:Tettigonilidae) in Zanzibar. Report, Plant Protection Research Coordinating Committee Meeting, Ministry of Agriculture, Tanzania. November 23, 1993.

Marshed, M.N; Rashid, A.A; Masoud, T; Salim, M.; Mwamvura, B. (1993) *Report by the Task Force of the Termite Problem in Zanzibar Agriculture*. Ministry of Agriculture, Zanzibar.

Martin, P.J. (1989) *Zanzibar Clove Cultivation Manual*. Zanzibar Clove Research Project. Ministry of Agriculture, Livestock and Natural Resources, Zanzibar.

Ministry of Agriculture and Livestock Zanzibar (1984) Agricultural and Livestock Policy.

Ministry of Agriculture and Livestock Zanzibar (1991) Agricultural and Livestock Policy Revision.

Oswald, S. (1985) Half year report on *Pseudotheraptus wayi* (Brown) (Heteroptera), Coreidae) research. National Coconut Development Programme, Pest Control Section, Zanzibar.

Oswald, S. (1988) Suitability of Endosulfan, Dimethoate and Formethoate for the Adhoc and Integrated Control of *Pseudotheraptus wayi* (Brown). National Coconut Development Programme Pest Control Section, Zanzibar.

Robbins, S.R.J. (1987) *Development in the World Market for Cloves, 1986/87*. Report to the Government of Tanzania (Zanzibar). Tropical Development Research Institute, London.

Van der Weel, J. (1992) *Heteronychus Control in Rainfed Rice in Zanzibar*. Plant Protection Division, Zanzibar.

Van Huis, A. (1991) *Report of a Backstopping Visit to the Plant Protection Project Zanzibar*. Wageningen Agricultural University, Department of Entomology.

Van Keulen, A. (1990) *Effects of Fertilizer and Insecticide on Stemborer Attack in Maize under Farmers' Conditions*. Wageningen, The Netherlands: Department of Entomology, Agricultural University.

Van Keulen, A.; Salim S.S.; Suleiman, Y. (1993) *Rice Hispa Beetle Research in Pemba*. Report of Annual Agricultural Research Review, Zanzibar.

Way, M.J. (1953) Studies on *Theraptus spp* (Coreidae) the cause of the gumming disease of coconuts in East Africa. *Bulletin of Entomological Research* **44**, 657-667.

Wirth, F.; Brosi, H.; Feiler-Jessenky, G.; Glasauer, P.; Krause, G.; Kunert, A.; Mdaihli, M. (1988) *A Baseline Survey for the Identification of Farming Systems in Zanzibar*. Center for Advanced Training in Agricultural Development, Technical University of Berlin.

PEST MANAGEMENT POLICIES IN LESS-DEVELOPED COUNTRIES

J.D. MUMFORD and J.M. STONEHOUSE

Imperial College Centre for Environmental Technology, Imperial College at Silwood Park, Ascot, Berkshire SL5 7PY, UK

ABSTRACT

All bodies responsible for social goals (governments, development donors, non-governmental organisations, etc.) need to establish policies by which they can achieve their goals. Problems associated with pests and pest management are of broad concern to society, and therefore warrant policy actions. However, there are several problems in developing pest and pest management policies. It is particularly difficult for groups within developing societies to agree on what their concerns and objectives are, and it is difficult to determine the best compromise policy to achieve the disparate goals of farmers, consumers, industrialists and others with an interest in pest management. The problem is further exacerbated by the imposition of policies on less-developed countries by outsiders who may act out of genuine concern for the environmental wellbeing of these countries, but who do not place the same values on present risk and future costs. It is important to develop baseline information on pest management practices and their impacts so that the consequences of pest management policies in less-developed countries can be evaluated in the future.

INTRODUCTION

Policies about pests and pest management form a small part of the overall responsibilities of governments and international institutions, yet they generate a substantial amount of discussion and agitation. Many deaths, billions of dollars, the preservation of our basic food supply and public health and the overall quality of the environment are at stake. It is not surprising that the subject is taken so seriously, but it may at first glance seem odd that there is so little agreement about what ought to be done and who should do it. This paper firstly discusses why governments are appropriate bodies to deal with pest management policies, then considers the options available to them, and finally suggests some implications for the future.

The existence of government is something that most people all over the world simply take for granted. Yet any discussion of the policy options of government may do well to begin by considering exactly why we have governments -- in general, what are they for? Ideally, a government is no more than a tool with a social purpose. Just as, say, a stock market is a tool for providing commerce with access to private capital, a government is a tool to allow society to regulate its affairs. Its core function is the provision of security, be it economic, legal, environmental, social, health, police or military. It is fitted to these functions because it is the best level of organization to control externalities. Externalities arise when the costs and benefits to the agent of a particular action are not the same as those to society at large. This imbalance may work either way. For example if a private trading

11

company were to raise a navy to protect its vessels from pirates, other merchant ships would enjoy some protection from it without having contributed to it, as "free riders": the private benefits are less than the social ones. On the other hand, if an industrial company pollutes the surrounding air or water, society bears costs greater than those of the company itself. Governments are a good way to organize activities to bring these differentials into line -- the suppression of piracy and the restraint of pollution are generally carried out by governments.

It follows that governments inevitably seek to control the behaviour of individuals. As this is understandably resented by the individuals concerned, government activity by its nature invites resistance, and societies generally are engaged in a perpetual debate over the relative pros and cons of a specific level of government control, as strong arguments for and against the powers of individuals enforce a fluid and shifting balance, with resulting compromises. This paradoxical property of government was well expressed by one of the first and greatest men to consider the question of what governments are for:

> "Some writers have so confounded society with government, as to leave little or no distinction between them; whereas they are not only different, but have different origins. Society is produced by our wants, and government by our wickedness; the former promotes our happiness positively by uniting our affections, the latter negatively by restraining our vices. The one encourages intercourse, the other creates distinctions. The first is a patron, the last a punisher.

> Society in every state is a blessing, but government even in its best state is but a necessary evil.... Government, like dress, is the badge of lost innocence; the palaces of kings are built on the ruins of the bowers of paradise.... Here then is the origin and rise of government; namely, a mode rendered necessary by the inability of moral virtue to govern the world...." (Paine, 1776).

Some may argue, however, that the control of pesticides, unique chemicals introduced into the environment specifically to kill organisms, is so crucial because of its implications for health and conservation of the environment, that it is not a suitable subject for the level of compromise inherent in much government policy formulation.

OBJECTIVES

The use of pesticides and agrochemicals is not the only source of concern within crop protection. There may be worries about the impact of plant breeding (Berry, 1990) and even biocontrol (for instance, legal action by environmentalists concerned with damage to non-target organisms, seen in the release of viruses at Oxford in 1994 for example, as recounted in almost all British newspapers daily during June, 1994). However, this paper concentrates mainly on the issues involved in pesticide management and policy.

In the field of pest management policy there are three major influence groups at work in the formation of policy.

● The public. The public has at least two interests in pest management policy. (a) It consumes the products which pest management protects, generally requiring that these products (most obviously food) be in sufficient supply and as cheap as possible. (b) It is also potentially exposed to the detrimental consequences of injudicious pest management -- particularly to pesticide residues in foods and the environment. In consequence, the public's requirement tends to be for reliable pest control, largely entailing pesticide use, tempered with strict controls to limit damaging use. (It is necessary, however, to distinguish the primary requirements in developed and less-developed countries.)

- Farmers. Like the public, farmers tend to have two different and not wholly compatible interests. (a) To protect their profits and livelihoods, farmers require pest control which is as effective and sustainable as possible. This tends to argue for the use of pesticides, but not necessarily the maximization of use. The susceptibility of pests to pesticides is a "common property resource" which individuals may exploit more heavily than is optimal for society as a whole, as the stimulation of resistance by pesticide overuse by a few farmers will have damaging effects on all. This is a classic case of differing private and social costs, and one where government intervention has brought clear benefits. (b) Farmers themselves are particularly at risk from the health consequences of injudicious pesticide use, from application processes and work in treated crops. Although these risks are generally personally borne, many farmers tend to take inadequate precautions, either because they lack information or on the principle that "familiarity breeds contempt", and many governments use their own tools, such as legislation, to encourage farmers to protect themselves.

- Manufacturers and traders of pesticides and pest control. These industries often form coherent and powerful political lobbies. Much has been written about the desirability and reality of the slow metamorphosis of the pesticide manufacturing industry into a service industry, providing and charging for integrated pest control, rather than making money solely from pesticide sales (Urech, 1990). If and when this process is complete, the interests of this industry may broadly coincide with those of farmers. Until it is complete, however, elements within the industry will tend to have their own agenda -- the maximisation of profits by the maximisation of pesticide sales. This and similar interests can manifest themselves in complex ways. For example, the governments of many less-developed countries have subsidised pesticide use in the past, in the interests of "agricultural development" (for example in Zanzibar, as described by Marshed-Kharusy, this volume). These subsidies are no longer as well-favoured as they once were, and many countries are withdrawing them, but an obstacle to this process is that the market distortions of subsidies, while they were in place, stimulated the pesticide manufacturing, distribution and retailing industries beyond the dictates of the free market, and these sectors sometimes face retrenchment and losses as subsidies are withdrawn, prompting their political resistance to the withdrawals (Repetto, 1985).

This list is not complete, as other interests sometimes impinge on the pest management debate. Inputs may also come from, for example, wildlife conservation enthusiasts, fishermen and hunters whose prey are affected by pesticides, financial institutions who have invested in farming or the pest control industry, and the operators of medical pest control programmes, whose actions may be undermined by pesticide resistance stimulated by agricultural pesticides.

These influences work to affect policy in two ways. Firstly, they may seek to influence government itself, by voting, agitation or lobbying. Secondly, they may seek to influence the government's supporters, and particularly its sources of finance. In the developing world these latter are of particular importance, as many governments there rely heavily on financial resources abroad, in the form of aid donors and capital lenders, be they foreign governments, foreign private banks or multilateral lenders such as the Bretton Woods organizations. These outside agencies wield considerable influence in less-developed countries, and have constituent interests of their own. In particular, answering largely to political influences in the developed world, they often tend, in the balancing of issues of "development" and "the environment", to favour the latter more than the political influences in the developing world itself.

There is, therefore, a need for efficient **pest** management with relatively low immediate costs and risks to producers and minimal long-term costs to the environment and consumers. There is also a need for management of **pest management**, to prevent adverse external effects that would otherwise be borne by society at large. Society has two major problems in achieving these objectives: it is not clear what they want (Mumford, 1993); and it is not clear what is the best way of achieving these goals (Ramirez and Mumford, 1994).

There are two main reasons for disagreement about what society wants from a policy on pest management (Norton & Mumford, 1993). The first is the complexity of many pest and pesticide problems. They can involve many different groups of organisms and reactions and interactions in the soil and water, which are difficult to understand and predict. This complexity can make it difficult to determine what the likely result of changing a management activity will be. The second problem involves the fact that there are different groups involved, with different objectives, and it is not merely a case of accepting an average objective for the groups. This is particularly important when pressures for policies to be implemented come from outside a country, based on value judgements that are legitimate and widely held in one place, but not in another.

Some problems arise in the management of pesticides and pests because of the imposition of objectives determined by outsiders, some of which may conflict with local values (Dahlberg, 1993). International organisations have generally promoted production-oriented agricultural systems which require substantial risk-reducing inputs, such as pesticides, rather than more sustainable, lower risk systems. More recently, "sustainability" has become the focus for many international agricultural development programmes, but often with definitions supplied by developed country agencies. There is further tension caused by environmentalists in developed countries, on the one hand, demanding strict adherence to, for example, US Environmental Protection Agency guidelines on pesticide use and, on the other hand, free trade interests who are trying to reduce costs through abolition of non-tariff barriers to trade (such as environmental and health standards). The immediate problems of income generation to keep up with rising populations and aspirations in less-developed countries often result in a short term view of environmental risks, which are often long term by nature.

Further complications are introduced by the issues of time scale and social discount rates, for example in the management of pesticide resistance. Individuals tend to discount the possible loss of a resource (such as susceptible pests) in the future, putting greater value on control in the present. However, society as a whole can take a much longer term view and has a much lower discount on future value. In this case the sum of the individual responses to a future need to reduce resistance is much less than the social optimum, and a strong political decision may be needed to overcome that difference.

Throughout the formation of pest and pest management policies there will be conflict and a need to compromise. Some issues involve moral responsibility (say to protect others from poisoning), while others could be resolved by economic means, such as compensation for groups whose immediate objectives are not met.

OPTIONS

The tools by which a government may carry out its functions are inherently of two sorts: activities whose social benefits are higher than their private ones may be encouraged; and those for which social costs are higher than their private ones may be discouraged. The use of pesticides is particularly paradoxical in this context. In some states and cases, their use is considered to be a social good and is stimulated by financial incentives. In others it is considered to be socially undesirable and is restrained, by bans or other limitations on use. This contradictory aspect of the use of pesticides, combined with imprecise thinking about exactly what their social benefits and costs are, has led to confusion in some cases of government pesticide policy, whereby some government actions may even counteract others.

In general terms, governments have five policy options (Stonehouse and Mumford, 1994): command, manipulate, direct, process and inform. Relatively little use is made of commands, such as pesticide bans, because of inadequate bureaucratic control to enforce them in many places. Farah (1993), in a review of pesticide policies in less-developed countries, considered that most less-developed countries have policies that actually encourage pesticide use, mainly by manipulating prices through subsidies, and through imbalances in the way they inform farmers and other pesticide users. Direction, that is simply stating what the objective of government is (for instance, the establishment of integrated pest management and the reduction of pesticide use) is increasingly being used, as in Indonesia and the Philippines, and even the USA. However, this appears to be most successful when it is backed up by a ban on undesirable pesticides and clear information widely disseminated on how to practise alternative pest management. Process-related policies, such as legislation to establish ways for resolving conflicts between groups favouring or opposing pest control, appear to be relatively infrequent.

Much of the attention to existing policies has been directed at pesticide subsidies (Farah, 1993; Waibel, 1989). The general principle is that pesticide use is determined by price, and that in countries where pesticide use is low it is often necessary to subsidise pesticides to encourage farmers to begin to use them. This may be caused by a particularly devastating pest outbreak, or may simply be part of an agricultural modernisation programme. Many argue that increasing pesticide prices will have the converse effect, and could be used to reduce use where it is deemed to be excessive. This is largely unproved, however, and is not necessarily intuitively likely. The dramatic reduction of pesticide use in Indonesia in the late 1980s (Waibel, 1989; Farah, 1993) arose through a combination of mechanisms: bans, a strong official proclamation of social direction, reduced subsidies, and farmer education on alternatives. The impact of eliminating the subsidies component may have been minimal.

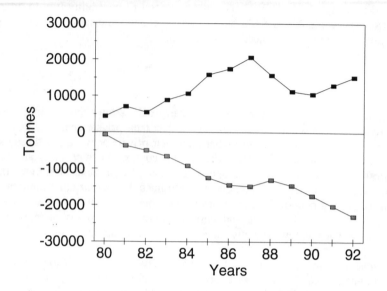

Figure 1. Pesticides imports (above) and use (below) in Pakistan.

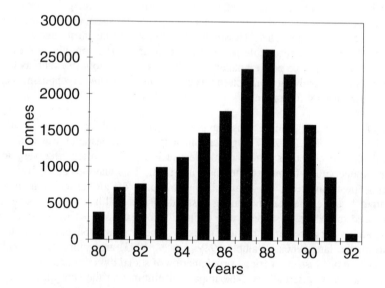

Figure 2. National pesticide balance in storage in Pakistan. Pesticide subsidies were reduced in 1988.

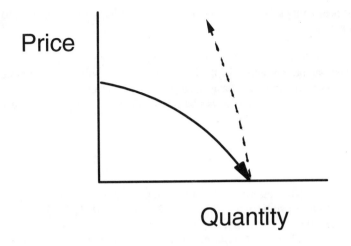

Figure 3. Proposed demand curves for novice pesticide users (solid) and experienced users (dashed).

In the case of Pakistan, eliminating pesticide subsidies in 1988 had no long-term effect on the trend in use (Figure 1), but it did have an effect on imports and the overall pesticide balance in the country (Figure 2). The effect of the subsidies, mainly of cotton insecticides during the 1980s, was to produce pesticide mountains in storage, not fields awash with sprays. A similar situation existed in Tanzania recently, as drums of subsidised pesticides piled up in remote villages. Subsidies may do more to distort markets at the level of government purchasing agencies than at the farm.

Why might higher prices not reduce use, after low prices have introduced farmers to pesticides? Pesticides, and indeed all pest control, are perceived to be risk-reducing inputs. They may, therefore, be perceived to be "essential", and be relatively inelastic in their demand. How many people would stop taking out insurance if the price doubled? We can hypothesise that the demand curve for pesticide use changes as users become more experienced (Figure 3). There is one curve for novices, quite sensitive to price, and another for experienced users, that is quite insensitive. Small price reductions stimulate initial use, but even large increases may not reduce established use.

IMPLICATIONS

Several implications arise from these issues. Firstly, there must be mechanisms to establish how trade-offs between interest groups can be reached. Without such effort pest and pest management policies will either continue to be avoided or will continue to be *ad hoc*.

Secondly, subsidies alone should not be the targets of pest management policy. Integrated policies, such as have been adopted in Indonesia, with a mixture of command, manipulation, direction and information, are much more likely to be successful than any individual response. The same is true for policies that involve farmer training alone. Unless training is backed up by other policy instruments it is unlikely to be adequate to achieve IPM implementation.

Finally, there is a need for baselines and indicators by which changes actually effected by new policies can be measured. Without such measures it will not be possible to determine how effective particular policies have been in various circumstances. They would also be essential in helping to predict the costs and likely effects of new pest and pest management policies.

REFERENCES

Berry, C.L. (1990) The hazards of healthy living - the agricultural component. *Brighton Crop Protection Conference - Pests and Diseases 1990*, **1**, 3-13.

Dahlberg, K.A. (1993). Government policies that encourage pesticide use in the United States. In: *The Pesticide Question: Environment, Economics, and Ethics*, D. Pimentel and H. Lehman (Eds). New York: Chapman and Hall.

Farah, J. (1993) *Pesticide Policies in Developing Countries; Do they Encourage Excessive Pesticide Use?* Washington, DC, USA: The World Bank.

Mumford, J.D. (1993) The economics of integrated pest control in protected crops. *Pesticide Science*, **36**, 379-383.

Norton, G.A.; Mumford, J.D. (Eds) (1993) *Decision Tools for Pest Management*. Wallingford, UK: CAB International.

Paine, T. (1776) *Common Sense*. 2nd edition. Philadelphia, PA, USA: W & T Bradford.

Ramirez, O.A.; Mumford, J.D. (1994) The role of policy action in support of more implementation of IPM in agricultural production. *Proceedings, IPM Working Group Implementation Workshop*, San Jose, Costa Rica, March 1994 (in press).

Repetto, R. (1985) *Paying the Price: Pesticide Subsidies in Developing Countries*. Washington, DC, USA: World Resources Institute.

Stonehouse, J.M.; Mumford, J.D. (1994) *Science, Risk Assessment and Environmental Decisions*. Geneva: United Nations Environment Programme.

Urech, P.A. (1990). Industry's achievements in meeting the needs of society and farmers for modern plant protection. *1990 British Crop Protection Conference - Pests and Diseases*, **1**, 283-292.

Waibel, H. (1989) Pesticide subsidies and the diffusion of IPM in rice in Southeast Asia: The case of Thailand. Paper presented at the 14th session of the FAO/UNEP Panel of Experts on Integrated Pest Control. Rome, Italy. October, 1989.

Session 2

Appropriate technology and training:
the way forward

REQUIREMENTS FOR THE SAFE AND EFFECTIVE MANAGEMENT OF PESTICIDES
IN LESS-DEVELOPED COUNTRIES

J. R. COX

Natural Resources Institute, Central Avenue, Chatham Maritime, Chatham, Kent ME4 4TB,
UK

ABSTRACT

The use of pesticides is subjected to increasing public scrutiny, reflected in
tighter national and international legislation. In the developed world, pesticide use
is tightly controlled and practices are generally good. The situation in less-
developed countries is often, however, quite different and although some
individual countries have made substantial progress in the development and
enforcement of pesticide-use legislation, with supporting monitoring facilities,
many are badly in need of substantial assistance for the provision of appropriate
technology and expertise to allow them to implement the necessary programmes.

INTRODUCTION

Pesticide use in less-developed countries is anecdotally synonymous with unsafe
practice, misuse and abuse. Registration systems are considered weak, extension services
under-manned and ill-informed, and facilities for the monitoring and policing of national and
international legislation are few or non-existent.

Although there is much truth in this, recognition must also be given to those national
authorities that are both active and effective, often functioning with minimal resources, and
who are showing just what can be done. Much comes down to initiative, determination and
the will to safeguard the public and the environment from pesticide misuse.

There is no doubt that there is a rapidly growing awareness of the risks associated with
the misuse of pesticides. However in most less-developed countries, where pesticides are
available and affordable, their continued use is essential for efficient crop production and
protection. Integrated pest management programmes are being developed which emphasise
improved cultural practices, and the use of biological control systems and natural pesticides
to reduce dependence on chemical pesticides. However, conventional chemical pesticides will
remain with us, for a wide range of uses, for the foreseeable future and we need to ensure
that management practices are substantially improved to accommodate their safe and efficient
use.

TECHNIQUES AND TECHNOLOGIES

Pesticide management and application

The safe and effective management of pesticides requires a high degree of training
coupled with a thorough understanding of all the issues involved in their choice,
procurement, storage and use. There are many good and professional managers involved with

the use of these materials who ensure that all reasonable precautions are taken to protect the user, the consumer and the environment. Unfortunately there is also a large proportion of poor managers who, for a variety of reasons, choose to ignore the basics of good pesticide management putting the environment and, more particularly, their fellow workers at risk.

The problem is not always limited to the smallholder, who for reasons of ignorance or lack of funds may purchase cheap, substandard products, who cannot afford protective clothing, or because he/she cannot read the label instructions, prepares treatment solutions by guesswork. Some large farms and estates also exhibit a very casual approach towards pesticide use and operator training, although generally their standards are much higher.

The choice of pesticide for particular pest or disease problems is often the point at which things begin to go wrong. Growers producing crops for the export market will generally operate to defined spray regimes and use pesticides from an agreed list of approved products. Others may receive less guidance and rely on advice from fellow growers, representatives of agrochemical companies or their own judgement. Pesticide choice can also be limited by cost or availability; trade across national boundaries in cheap, banned products can become a significant factor in border areas under such circumstances.

A further range of scenarios can unfold when pesticide packaging is considered. Although standards are improving and the use of pictograms is helpful, problems still occur through poor labelling, labelling in the wrong language and illiteracy on the part of the user. Poor labelling practices often arise when pesticides are formulated or repackaged within country; registration authorities need to be more alert to this. All these factors can contribute to the misuse of the product. In many cases little harm results, but in others the consequences can be serious and deaths have resulted.

The stores in which agrochemicals are frequently kept before, after and between use are a further potential source of accident and error. Many of us have seen, I am sure, products kept in the home, sometimes in plain containers and bottles which could be, and have been, mistaken for drink or for cooking materials. The chances of accidental poisoning in these circumstances are high. By contrast there are also farms which have separate, locked stores with secure shelving, dispensing facilities, spillage control, protective clothing, stock records and water for personal decontamination. In between these two extremes lies a wide range of indifferent practices which can result in mistakes and misuse. The commonest problem is one of poor stock control where new materials are put at the front of the shelf and used first, whilst the older material, usually opened and part used, remains on the shelf, slowly deteriorating before it is eventually used. Mixing of products on a single shelf is also a common sight, allowing every opportunity for the wrong product to be taken and used.

The choice and use of protective equipment, especially in tropical conditions, is a particular problem. Reasons for not using such equipment vary between cost, indifference and the discomfort of wearing the equipment under a hot sun. Lighter, cooler alternatives exist but the use of protective clothing, particularly by smallholders, is poor and is probably the single largest factor in many of the alarmingly high number of reported cases of pesticide poisoning.

Application equipment and practices vary considerably in many developing countries and the whole spectrum from good to bad can often be seen in a short space of time. The commonest fault observed is the use of inappropriate or poorly maintained equipment. Care taken in product selection, solution/suspension preparation and in the application itself can be wasted if the delivery rates or the drop spectrum are incorrect. How many of us have seen punctured coins or washers used to replace nozzle discs on sprayers? How much or how little sprayer calibration is undertaken?

Lack of education and training in the discipline of safe and effective pesticide application is a major issue. In recognition of this, the International Group of National Associations of Manufacturers of Agrochemical Products (GIFAP) has developed its Safe Use Project (Ledru *et al.*, this volume). GIFAP will admit, however, that this merely scratches the surface of the problem and that major initiatives to address the subject of pesticide management and use must be undertaken if improvements are to be made. Such training needs to be aimed at two distinct levels:

- For the supervisor/manager primarily responsible for the handling, storage and supervision of agrochemical use.

- For the operators involved in the preparation and application of agrochemicals.

There are areas of overlap between these but also some quite distinct differences. The supervisor needs to be able to manage effectively all stages in the operation: procurement, stock record maintenance, storage, issue and measurement of pesticides and the supervision of spray activities. He/she will also have to be fully conversant with all of the activities of the operator who, although focusing on a narrower range of activities, will need to be proficient in the safe and effective preparation of treatment solutions, correct application procedures, equipment cleaning and maintenance and personal safety. These issues will be dealt with in greater depth later in the conference proceedings associated with this Symposium.

Monitoring and analysis

Residues
Effective monitoring of pesticide use and the detection of cases of misuse (including over- and underdosing, lack of observance of the pre-harvest interval and the use of illegal pesticides) and of environmental contamination, requires access to supporting analytical facilities. Similarly, national research into improved application techniques or modified application regimes to combat particular pest problems or complexes requires analytical support.

Some developing countries have introduced good quality analytical laboratories, sometimes with donor support, others have no facilities at all. The reasons for this are varied, and include the lack of suitably qualified, trained staff, but there is no doubt that those countries with a substantial or developing horticultural export trade have had the incentive to develop full and appropriate laboratory services; in the current climate of competition between producing nations and in the face of ever-stricter legislation on Maximum Residue Levels (MRLs), the detection of excessive or illegal residues in foodstuffs, by an importing country, could jeopardise future trade links.

The problem faced by many laboratories, and the largest single factor restricting their establishment and maintenance, is one of cost. Quite apart from the set-up costs, which can be prohibitive, there are the increased costs of maintenance where the laboratory is remote from service facilities in the region, and the cost of general consumable materials, particularly solvents and other chemical reagents. For many countries these need to be imported and there are, additionally, problems of supply and logistics which need to be addressed. In some cases these problems are insoluble; in others the basic choice of equipment may be a factor and a more considered choice based on reliability, local service arrangements, minimum of replaceable parts, reduced material consumption etc. may improve the viability of the laboratory and reduce instrument downtime.

Technologies and procedures used by the different laboratories depend essentially on the laboratory's function -- whether support of research studies on one or two known compounds or multi-residue screening of export crops prior to shipment. These laboratories can be poles apart in terms of the complexity and breadth of the techniques used and the equipment required. Analytical procedures commonly used in Europe or the United States may not be appropriate or affordable to some of these laboratories in terms of material requirements.

There is a desperate need for a re-evaluation of analytical practices to meet the competing demands of the analyst seeking ever-smaller limits of analytical detection and using the most sophisticated of methods to achieve them, and the needs of overseas laboratories where the nature of the analysis, and the equipment/material requirements, puts it almost beyond their capabilities. Whilst recognising the need to analyse for extremely low residues and that sometimes there is no alternative, there is a tendency for analysts to use the most sophisticated procedure rather than a more mundane one that could achieve the same result. Similarly, there is a tendency to create new methods of analysis whereas the same result may be achievable by expanding the use of an existing procedure.

There is also scope for the development and use of simplified screening procedures. The use of such procedures is something of a bone of contention with some analysts. Many insist on the principle that *if you are going to do the job, you've got to do it properly* and that laboratories must use a standard, fully validated procedure without any *corner cutting*. Whilst the principle of only using validated procedures is absolutely correct, there is scope for simplified procedures for screening as long as they too are properly validated and their limitations are known. Samples containing residues detected with such a procedure and at a level near to the reporting level or to the MRL can be re-examined as necessary, using a full reference procedure. In this way, the analytical integrity can be maintained whilst at the same time the analytical throughput can be increased and the costs to the laboratory decreased.

There are, regrettably, few such methods published and accepted by the scientific community. Many others exist, I am sure, unpublished, but used in routine national or other surveillance programmes. We need to make these methods more widely available or provide resources for their development if we are to promote the development of residue analysis in developing country laboratories.

Thin-layer chromatography (TLC) is a relatively low-cost technique which may well be appropriate for some routine screening activities and deserves increased attention. Although used extensively in India and parts of Europe, interest in TLC seems to have waned somewhat although some excellent new coatings have been developed. A wide range of chromogenic reagents have been evaluated and excellent results achieved for most pesticides. This work is well documented in the scientific literature, providing a sound basis for uptake and development by interested laboratories.

The use of test kits based on cholinesterase or enzyme-linked immunosorbent assay (ELISA) may also have a role to play although their relevance to multi-residue screening is limited. For particular analyses, especially those using the more specific ELISA procedures, there may be distinct advantages and their use should be considered, although it is important that the limitations of the procedures are known and understood (Cox, 1993).

Formulated products

Similarly, there are relatively few developing country laboratories involved in the quality control of formulated pesticides. The relevant analytical procedures for both chemical and physical properties are well defined, and of necessity, standardised. Equipment needs vary and can utilise a range of analytical techniques; for those countries using a wide range of formulated products, the requirements can be high and, accordingly, the establishment of a quality control laboratory can be difficult to fund. The importance, however, of effective quality control cannot be stressed enough.

Old and deteriorated materials and substandard or wrongly labelled products must be detected and eliminated through effective quality assurance programmes supported by active legislation. If used, such products bring the agrochemical industry into disrepute, cause financial losses to growers, help the development of pest resistance and can lead to rejection of exported horticultural produce. Unscrupulous dealers will continue to sell such products until they know that quality testing is being carried out and that they run the risk of being detected and prosecuted. An excellent example of the benefits of introducing such a programme comes from Costa Rica where, in 1988, a Quality Control Laboratory within the Ministry of Agriculture and Livestock was established with the help of the German Agency for Technical Cooperation (GTZ). Following the introduction of a rigorous quality monitoring programme, the percentage of samples of formulated product meeting national standards in terms of active ingredient content rose from 43% in 1989 to 88% in 1992 (Mesen and von Dueszelen, 1993). When physical properties are included the comparable figures are 32% in 1989 and 80% in 1992. Similar experiences have been reported elsewhere.

The agrochemical industry is a large one and competition for sales is fierce; some small companies, often regrettably in less-developed countries, capitalise on this by producing cut-price products at the expense of product quality. These practices must be detected and stopped through the introduction of effective national quality assurance systems.

TRAINING

Thorough and effective training of all personnel involved in the management and use of pesticides is essential. This should start with the most senior member of the organisation and proceed down towards those responsible for day-to-day operations. The resulting training requirements must be met through international cooperation and the sharing of experience and expertise. Training should only be delivered by competent authorities and not be seen as just another business opportunity by those with minimal expertise but with a good public relations image. Unfortunately this is all too common an occurrence in the developing world where profits are made at the expense of those who can least afford it.

Training should be viewed as an asset and not as a distraction; it is time well spent. Of particular importance are the requirements for training in pesticide analytical techniques, where training inputs are much less than they should be. The training period depends upon the abilities of the individual and his/her projected duties. For an inexperienced chemist expected to be capable of analysing a wide range of pesticides, a minimum of three -- and preferably six -- months' training is recommended. This training must be under the supervision of an experienced, senior analyst and be part of a practically oriented course supplemented by discussion/seminars as new topics are introduced. Pesticide analysis is a subject requiring much practice and cannot be taught from behind a desk. The facilities should, where possible, reflect the equipment to be used by the student on return home. Where this is not possible, he/she must be familiar with all the operations such that there are no difficulties in switching between different makes or models of equipment.

Training requirements should also include inputs on basic equipment installation and servicing, preferably from the manufacturer of the equipment in question, and preventative maintenance and diagnostic testing. Such training is important for the maximisation of instrument usage and to minimise downtime through simple faults that could be easily remedied, or prevented, by basic training. Any additional training costs incurred will, in the long term, benefit the laboratory concerned.

The further requirement for laboratories to be accredited or to work to Good Laboratory Practice (GLP) adds extra pressure, particularly for those laboratories providing surveillance data, monitoring export crops or providing analytical back-up to research for international product registration. The discipline required for this is strict and depends on a thorough understanding of all the factors associated with an analytical laboratory. It will be very difficult for new laboratories to conform to GLP in the early stages of their lives unless they are staffed or managed by senior analysts already familiar with the requirements. Accreditation to international standards or full GLP will not be an option for many such developing country laboratories in the foreseeable future, and for most there is a need to introduce a half-way house. In this, the standards would still be high; the principles of GLP would be operated with the laboratories also participating in collaborative ring exercises. The introduction and recognition of such a standard is important, however, if the laboratories are to be recognised as a source of reputable data and their development encouraged.

The future career development of good quality, trained staff must also not be neglected. There are many examples of where the lack of reward or motivation for such staff has led to their loss to other employment, with the efficiency of their departments suffering in consequence. Good staff, trained in the relevant technical disciplines, are difficult to replace and there is, inevitably, a considerable time lag in training them to a comparable standard.

CONCLUSIONS

In summary, and without wishing to minimise the substantial progress made by some individual countries, there are many challenges for the nations of the developing world to address before safe and effective pesticide management can be achieved. Training and equipment requirements must be met, effective accommodation and test areas must be provided and the implications of national and international legislation must be understood. Modern technology has a role to play in supporting these processes, but care needs to be taken in its selection such that the most appropriate is chosen for the situation rather than what may be the latest development in the field. Procedural developments, often demand-led from the developed nations, must bear in mind that there are many other potential users and that their needs must be similarly addressed.

REFERENCES

Cox, J.R. (1993) The role of test kits in pesticide residue analysis. *Conference Proceedings, Postharvest News and Information*, **4**, 23-24.

Mesen, S.; von Dueszelen, J. (1993) Quality control of pesticides in Costa Rica. *Pesticide Outlook*, **4**, 14-15.

BIOLOGICAL CONTROL OF INSECT PESTS AND WEEDS IN THAILAND: A CHALLENGE AND A THEORY OF MULTIPLE EFFORTS

BANPOT NAPOMPETH

National Biological Control Research Centre (NBCRC), Kasetsart University and National Research Council of Thailand, Bangkok 10900, Thailand

ABSTRACT

Crop protection practices in the developing world are generally presumed to be primitive, inappropriate and inadequately scientific, according to the standards of the developed world. Such cultural intimidation is also applied to the biological control practices being developed or already accomplished in the developing world. In contrast to such negative assumptions, the accomplishments in biological control of insect pests and weeds in Thailand, one of the less-developed countries, are presented. Some successes are listed with reference to theories of biological control, where applicable. The necessity for multiple efforts is stressed to encourage fellow countries in the developing world to confront crop protection problems, relying on biological control either as a single control measure, or as a major component in integrated pest management systems.

INTRODUCTION

Economically the world has been sharply divided into the rich and the poor, the North and the south, the East and the West, the First and the Third World, the developed and the developing, the more affluent and the less fortunate, and so on. Such economic divisions are obviously made from the materialistic viewpoint, and fail to consider other parameters such as culture, way of life, climatic and biological factors.

Likewise, crop protection, or the struggle against insect pests, diseases, weeds and other pest problems, has also been similarly divided such that the crop protection methods in developed countries are regarded as superior to those currently practised in the less-developed countries, labelled as the "Third World". This assumption has been repeated continually in the crop protection literature, and has also been deeply rooted both in the minds of westerners who have little knowledge of crop protection, and in the minds of qualified crop protection experts in various national and international development and assistance agencies. But are there significant differences in the crop protection practices employing certain synthetic chemicals: their effects on users; their target and non-target organisms; and their effects on the environment in the developed and developing worlds? The same question can be addressed to other crop protection practices, including those using non-chemical methods such as biological control.

This paper presents a challenge to the conventional view of crop protection in the developing world and emphasizes the need for multiple efforts, by drawing supporting evidence from various attempts at the biological control of insect pests and weeds in Thailand. For this purpose it is appropriate to consider various definitions of biological control, and to refer to some theories of biological control and relate them to current practices.

DEFINITIONS OF BIOLOGICAL CONTROL

Classical biological control is defined as "the action of parasites, predators, or pathogens in maintaining another organism's population density at a lower average than would occur in their absence" (DeBach, 1964). It can be *disciplinary*, defined as "the study and utilization of parasites, predators and pathogens for the regulation of host population densities" (DeBach, 1964), further simplified as "the utilization of natural enemies to reduce the damage caused by noxious organisms to the tolerable level" (DeBach & Ronsen, 1991). With the advent of rDNA technology, genetic engineering and biotechnology, biological control has been defined and modified as "the use of natural or modified organisms, genes, or gene products to reduce the effects of undesirable organisms (pests), and to favour desirable organisms such as crops, trees, animals, and beneficial insects and microorganisms" (NAS, 1988); this description is referred to here as *augmentative* biological control. With the worldwide attempts to search for alternatives to pesticides, biological control has been described as "any pest control measure not employing synthetic chemical pesticides". The latter definition embraces other biology-based control measures such as host resistance, botanical pesticides, use of insect growth regulators, etc., all of which have been coined as *parabiological control* by Sailer (1981).

From these definitions, van den Bosch *et al.* (1982) preferred a concept of biological control that embraces other control measures, and regarded the definition of biological control in DeBach (1964) as a classical and traditional one. The definition of biological control by the National Academy of Sciences (NAS, 1988) has also received wide objections from numerous conventional biological control workers worldwide.

It has been strictly in the context of these definitions that attempts to develop biological control in Thailand have followed the route from DeBach's (1964) definition through that of DeBach & Rosen (1991), and to a very large extent through that of Sailer (1981), and are venturing at an increasing pace into that of NAS (1988). The trend of research and development in biological control in Thailand has thus far progressed in the same manner as in developed countries.

BIOLOGICAL CONTROL OF INSECT PESTS AND WEEDS IN THAILAND

Systematic research and development for the implementation of biological control in Thailand was not initiated until 1975, when the National Biological Control Research Centre (NBCRC) was established with support from the National Research Council of Thailand, and implemented by Kasetsart University in collaboration with 17 other national institutions comprising various universities, government agencies and enterprises. In addition to its headquarters located at the Bangkhen (Bangkok) campus of Kasetsart University, NBCRC has established regional centres: Central at Kasetsart University, Kamphaengsaen Campus (Nakhon Pathom); Northern at Maejo University in Chiangmai; Northeastern at Khon Khaen University (Khon Khaen); and Southern at Prince of Songkla University, Hat Yai, Songkla. With the headquarters, these NBCRC regional centres serve as focal points for research and development activities and implementation of biological control projects specific to regional insect pest and weed problems.

Prior to the establishment of NBCRC, attempts at biological control carried out in Thailand were negligible. The first accounts on the parasitic Hymenoptera in Thailand included reports by Ladell (1930, 1931, 1933a,b) in one of which a eulophid egg parasite, *Tetrastichus schoenobii,* was found attacking rice stem borer. It was not until 1963 that the very first attempt at classical biological control was made when a scolid wasp, *Scolia ruficornis*, was introduced from the then Caroline Islands for the control of the coconut rhinoceros beetle, *Oryctes rhinoceros.* This was soon followed in 1965 by the introduction of *Brachymeria* sp., *Cotesia plutellae, Tetrastichus sokolowskii,* and *Diadromus (Thyraella) collaris* from India for the control of the diamondback moth, *Plutella xylostella.* An event that helped place Thailand on the world map of biological control took place in 1974, when a braconid larval parasite, *Cotesia erionotae,* was introduced from Thailand to Hawaii resulting in complete control of the banana skipper, *Erionota thrax,* in the Hawaiian Islands. *C. erionotae* was later introduced to Papua New Guinea, resulting in highly satisfactory control of the banana skipper.

Substantial achievements in biological control of insect pests and weeds in Thailand since 1975 have been reviewed by Napompeth (1982) and updated by Napompeth (1989, 1990a,b, 1992a,b). Details of some of these accomplishments are given in NBCRC publications as extension leaflets, technical bulletins, special and miscellaneous publications and research reports. Such accomplishments in biological control encompass both augmentative and classical biological control of insect pests and weeds, and the use of biological control as a major component of integrated pest management systems.

Within a span of about three decades, a less-developed country such as Thailand has been able to build up specialized infrastructure and other supportive mechanisms, enabling the country to initiate, use and share its natural enemy resources, and to implement, collaborate and sustain biological control activities in a self-sufficient manner to such an extent that NBCRC has been considered as the key "natural enemy" of chemical control advocates and chemical companies within Thailand.

SOME THEORIES OF BIOLOGICAL CONTROL

The discussion of biological control concepts and questions by Doutt & DeBach (1964) describes a number of theories of biological control: the *sequence theory* of Howard and Fiske (1911), criticized by Thompson (1923); the *island theory* related to Imms' ecological islands (Imms, 1931); and the *three-generation* or *three-year theory* of Clausen (1951). Other theories relating to biological control are the *theory of new and old association* of Hokkanen & Pimentel (1984), and the *refuge theory* of Hawkins *et al.* (1993). All these theories were proposed in connection with classical biological control, where introductions of natural enemies are the main activities. Waage (1990) also attempted to justify the application of ecological theory in two approaches to the selection of biological control agents for introduction: *reductionist* and *holistic*. The theories propounded in biological control may or may not be applicable in a practical situation, because in many cases sufficient evidence is lacking.

How important are the better-known theories in biological control: the sequence theory, the island theory and the three-generation or three-year theory, for example, to less-developed countries in their attempts to initiate and develop biological control programmes? The less-developed countries can draw upon the experiences of the developed countries to improve their own programmes, by attempting the successes achieved through repeated effort, and avoiding the mistakes or failures previously experienced elsewhere.

The sequence theory

The sequence theory of Howard & Fiske (1911) states that with the gypsy moth or the brown-tail moth, parasitic (biological) control must come about through a variety of parasites, working together harmoniously, rather than through one specific parasite. The theory was challenged and criticized by Thompson (1923) who stated that, while a sequence of parasites may sometimes be desirable, nevertheless a single effective parasite on one stage of the host may well bring about control. Biological control of the banana skipper, *E. thrax*, in Thailand, Hawaii, Guam and Papua New Guinea could provide supporting evidence to Howard & Fiske (1911) as well as Thompson (1923).

In Thailand, *E. thrax* was parasitized by a number of parasitic insects. The more dominant and effective ones were the egg parasite, *Ooencyrtus erionotae*, the larval parasite, *Cotesia erionotae*, and a number of pupal parasites of which the chalcid *Brachymeria excarinata* dominated. The banana skipper is thus a good target for augmentative biological control in its native range, using a sequence of agents already available. Both *O. erionotae* and *C. erionotae* were introduced from Thailand to Hawaii and Guam but it turned out that *C. erionotae* was the more effective agent, contributing to the complete control of *E. thrax* in Hawaii but only substantial control in Guam. *C. erionotae* was later chosen as an agent and introduced from Guam to Papua New Guinea, where more or less complete control was achieved. Thus the sequence theory was at work in Thailand, while a single parasite on one stage of the host was also effective in Hawaii, Guam and Papua New Guinea.

An issue of importance in classical biological control is single *versus* multiple introductions. Parasites for diamondback moth control with single introductions to the country were *C. plutellae* (firmly established); *Macromalon orientale* (only recovered after a lapse of almost three decades); *Diadegma insulare* from Canada in 1964, *D. semiclausum* from Taiwan in 1989; and *T. sokolowskii* from India in 1976 and Pakistan in 1981-82. An egg parasite, *Trichogrammatoidea bactrea fumata*, found attacking the diamondback moth in Thailand, was also introduced to Taiwan in 1988.

A single-introduction approach was also adopted when the mottled water hyacinth weevil, *Neochetina eichhorniae*, was introduced from Florida to Thailand in 1977. It was not until 1990, when *N. eichhorniae* had become widely distributed in Thailand and had moved to neighbouring countries including Malaysia, that the second species of the chevroned water hyacinth weevil, *N. bruchi*, was introduced from Florida via Australia. Both the weevils are complementary in biological control of water hyacinth in Thailand.

A multiple-introduction approach was adopted in biological control of the giant sensitive plant, *Mimosa pigra*. The introduced agents were the seed bruchids, *Acanthoscelides puniceus* and *A. quadridentatus*; the top-shoot-feeding chrysomelid, *Chlamisus mimosae*; the young flower-bud-feeding apion, *Coeloecephalapion aculeatum*; and the stem-boring sesiid,

Carmenta mimosa, from South America via Australia. Of these introduced agents the seed bruchids are doing a very good job while others have not shown much promise. The same bruchids released in Northern Territory, Australia, did not perform as well as their counterparts in Thailand. Here the frequency of field releases could make a difference: since their introduction into Thailand in 1983, multiple field releases have been made consistently until the present.

The island theory

The island theory was based on the striking successes of biological control in the islands of Hawaii and Fiji, and in Imms' ecological islands (Imms, 1931) such as California. The island theory attempts to confirm and limit classical biological control methods to the insular areas, and suggests that biological control projects in non-insular areas are likely to meet with failure. The theory has received objections from biological control workers on the grounds that the successes in biological control in Hawaii, Fiji or California are not necessarily due to their insular location.

Thailand, although located on the Southeast Asian continent, could be considered an ecological island from a geographic and topographic point of view. Thus, according to the island theory, the country should be suitable for classical biological control. However, some of the classical biological control projects carried out in the country have met with failure. Examples are the failure to become established of several introduced parasitic Hymenoptera for the control of the diamondback moth, in spite of repeated introductions and field releases; and the failure of an arctiid moth, *Pareuchaetes pseudoinsulata*, introduced from Guam for the control of the exotic Siam weed, *Chromolaena odorata*, to become established although field releases covering diversified habitats were made.

In reality, most biological control projects, augmentative or classical, are carried out in locations and habitats with ecological limits and boundaries, the so-called *ecological islands*. It should be emphasized that it is mainly determination, combined with effort and given resources, that will generate success in biological control attempts no matter whether the country is geographically insular or not.

The three-generation or three-year theory

The three-generation or three-year theory of Clausen (1951) states that an effective parasite or predator might be expected to show evidence of control at the point of release within a period of three host generations or three years. The three-year theory is obviously applicable to target pests for biological control in temperate regions where most insects are univoltine. Under tropical conditions three generations could take much less than a year, and thus the three-generation theory would be more applicable. This theory is here restricted to the introduction, liberation and establishment of natural enemies in classical biological control, and has received both support and criticism.

Several coccinellids introduced to Thailand could not be recovered at all after field releases. Two coccinellids introduced and released for the control of the *Leucaena* psyllid, *Heteropsylla cubana*, behave differently: while *Curinus coeruleus* became established in less than a year but after several prey generations, *Olla v-nigrum* was found established once in one location in abundance but disappeared altogether afterwards. An encyrtid nymphal parasite, *Psyllaephagus yaseeni*, introduced for the same purpose, was firmly established in less than a year and certainly after several host generations. There is no clear explanation in a situation like this why the two coccinellids performed differently within the same habitat, while in Hawaii, where they had also been introduced a long time previously from Mexico, both *C. coeruleus* and *O. v-nigrum* do occupy the same habitat but with different population densities. Efforts were also made to introduce *O. v-nigrum* from Tonga to Thailand, but its fate was the same as before.

In classical biological control of weeds, the three-generation or three-year theory has to be modified. While the three-generation theory could apply to annual weeds, it will definitely not be applicable to perennial weeds; in the latter case the three-year theory would be more acceptable. Two weevils introduced for the control of water hyacinth in Thailand, *N. eichhorniae* and *N. bruchi,* showed obvious evidence of their establishment in less than a year. The same evidence was also obtained with the releases of two seed bruchids, *A. puniceus* and *A. quadridentatus*, for the control of the giant sensitive plant, *M. pigra.* However, the top-shoot-feeding chrysomelid, *C. mimosae,* was discovered in less than a year at the point of release only once and has not been found since.

Some parasitic Hymenoptera introduced for the control of the diamondback moth in the mid-1960s could not be traced. Among these parasites, only *C. plutellae* and *M. orientale* were discovered again in the early 1990s. This is caused not by the parasites themselves, but rather by failure to monitor them using the concept of the three-generation or three-year theory. No matter how superficial the theory, its application in classical biological control would be of help in terms of timely evaluation of the project. In any case, the project should not be assumed discontinued after three host generations or three years in compliance with the theory. In almost all biological control projects, additional and cumulative efforts would be worthwhile as long as such an effort is cost-effective and justifiable.

Other theories of biological control

Other theories of biological control worth mentioning are the theory of old and new association of Hokkanen & Pimentel (1984), and the refuge theory of Hawkins *et al.* (1993). So far there are no cases of biological control in Thailand which relate to the theory of old and new association. However, in the evaluation of the success or failure of various biological control projects, the refuge theory is highly applicable. Using a model proposed by Hawkins *et al.* (1993), it is possible to quantify the extent that parasites will depress host populations below the densities that hosts could achieve in the absence of parasites. The refuge theory predicts that hosts which occupy small refuges (that is, a low proportion of their population is in the refuges) will be highly exploitable by parasites, and as a result the host population will be severely reduced; conversely, for hosts that occupy sufficiently large refuges, parasites will be unable to exploit the host population sufficiently to depress its density appreciably. The theory concludes that the success of biological controls is inversely related to the proportion of insects protected from parasitism.

However, the refuge theory does not take into consideration the basic nature of biological control agents as the density-dependent mortality factor. In a refuge, large or small, density-dependent action is always in operation and self-destined in accordance with the population size, large or small. However, in the absence of substantial quantitative evidence to analyse, there is a need to ascertain whether the refuge theory could be used to evaluate the success of biological control projects.

ACHIEVING SUCCESS BY MULTIPLE EFFORTS

The development of biological control in Thailand has passed through a primitive phase lacking direction, to a phase in which systematic approaches were adopted and substantial achievements have been accomplished, to the extent that it can serve as a model for other countries in the developing world to follow. In all cases, in reference both to single successful projects and to overall biological control research and development activities, these achievements were the outcome of coordinated and multiple efforts. The various case studies in biological control of insect pests and weeds in Thailand, described above in relation to definitions and theories or biological control of insect pests and weeds, demonstrate the need for multiple efforts. It is the author's experience that *the more effort one devotes to the development of matters related to and supportive of biological control in terms of cost-efficiency and resources, the more likely are the successful achievement and desirable accomplishment in biological control regardless of any anticipated limitation and constraint. Multiple efforts should include multiple introductions and multiple parasites where appropriate.* The national profile on biological control of insect pests and weeds in Thailand serves to validate this statement.

CONCLUSIONS

In less-developed countries, the failure to initiate biological control projects is primarily due to the myth that biological control is expensive and difficult to achieve, and requires enormous investment and manpower, while the chances of success are remote and highly unpredictable. The governments of less-developed countries (or even developed countries) are very hesitant to provide adequate support for biological control projects. In this situation, a gap can be identified, which opens up the opportunity for outside expertise to enter, at a cost out of proportion to local and national standards, and still with no guarantee of success. Less-developed countries desiring to carry out biological control projects are thus toured by "safari" experts trying to convince the least knowledgeable high-ranking government officials and policy makers to accept their services at cost. The proposed commitment of multiple efforts needs to be applied to enable biological control projects to be economically realizable, and to enable competence in biological control to become deeply rooted and proliferated in the developing world.

ACKNOWLEDGEMENTS

The author would like to express his sincerest thanks to Dr Robert Black of the Natural Resources Institute for the initial idea to contribute to the Pre-Conference Symposium on Crop Protection in the Developing World at the 1994 Brighton Conference, and to the British Crop Protection Council for making his participation possible.

REFERENCES

van den Bosch, R.; Messenger, P.S.; Gutierrez, A.P. (1982) *An Introduction to Biological Control*. New York: Plenum.

Clausen, C.P. (1951) The time factor in biological control. *Journal of Economic Entomology*, **44**, 1-9.

DeBach, P. (Ed) (1964) *Biological Control of Insect Pests and Weeds*. New York: Reinhold.

DeBach, P.; Rosen, D. (1991) 2nd Edn. *Biological Control by Natural Enemies*. Cambridge: Cambridge University Press.

Doutt, R.L.; DeBach, P. (1964) Some biological control concepts and questions. In: *Biological Control of Insect Pests and Weeds*, P. DeBach (Ed), New York: Reinhold.

Hawkins, B.A.; Thomas, M.B.; Hochberg, M.E. (1993) Refuge theory and biological control. *Science* **262**, 1429-1432.

Hokkanen, H.; Pimentel, D. (1964) New approach for selecting biological control agents. *Canadian Entomologist*, **116**, 1109-1121.

Howard, L.O.; Fiske, W.F. (1911) The importation into the United States of the parasites of gypsy moth and the brown-tail moth. (United States Department of Agriculture) *Bureau of Entomology Bulletin*, **91**, 1-312.

Imms, A.D. (1931) *Recent Advances in Entomology*. London: Churchill.

Ladell, W.R.S. (1930) *Insects*. Bangkok, Thailand: Ministry of Lands and Agriculture.

Ladell, W.R.S. (1931) A new parasitic Hymenoptera. *Journal of Siam Society, Natural History Supplement*, **8**, 215.

Ladell, W.R.S. (1933a) A new parasite of paddy stem borers. *Journal of Siam society, Natural History Supplement*, **9**, 152.

Ladell, W.R.S. (1933b) Insects injurious to rice in Siam. *Journal of Siam Society, Natural History Supplement*, **9**, 161-172.

Napompeth, B. (1982) Biological control research and development in Thailand. In: *Proceedings of International Conference on Plant Protection in the Tropics*, K.L. Heong, B.S. Lee, T.M. Lim, C.H. Teoh and Yusof Ibrahim (Eds). Kuala Lumpur, Malaysia: Malaysian Plant Protection Society, pp. 301-323.

Napompeth, B. (1989) Biological control of insect pests and weeds in Thailand. In: *Biological Control of Pests*, BIOTROP Special Publication No. 36, Bogor, Indonesia, pp. 51-68.

Napompeth, B. (1990a) Biological control of weeds in Thailand. In: *Weed Management*, BIOTROP Special Publication No. 38, Bogor, Indonesia, pp. 23-36.

Napompeth, B. (1990b) Use of natural enemies to control agricultural pests in Thailand. In: *The Use of Natural Enemies to Control Agricultural Pests*. Taiwan: Food and Fertilizer Technology Centre Book Series No. 40, pp. 8-29.

Napompeth, B. (1992a) Brief review of biological control activities in Thailand. In: *Biological Control in Southeast Asia*, Y. Hirose (Ed), Fukuoka: Kyushu University Press, pp. 51-68.

Napompeth, B. (1992b) Biological control of paddy and aquatic weeds. In: *Biological Control and Integrated Management of Paddy and Aquatic Weeds in Asia*, Proceedings of International Symposium on Biological Control of Paddy and Aquatic Weeds in Asia, National Agricultural Research Centre, Tsukuba, Japan, pp. 249-258.

NAS (1988) *Research Briefings 1987*. Washington D.C.: National Academy of Sciences Press, pp. 56-68.

Sailer, R.I. (1981) Extent of biological control and cultural control of insect pests of crops. In: *Handbook of Pest Management in Agriculture,* D. Pimentel (Ed), Baco Raton: CRC Press, pp. 57-67.

Thompson, W.R. (1923) A criticism of the "sequence" theory of parasitic control. *Annals of the Entomological Society of America,* **16**, 115-128.

Waage, J. (1990) Ecological theory and the selection of biological control agents. In: *Critical Issues in Biological Control,* M. Mackauer, L.E. Ehler and J. Roland, (Eds), Andover: Intercept, pp. 135-157.

BIOTECHNOLOGY AND THE PROSPECTS FOR IMPROVING CROP RESISTANCE

V.A. HILDER and W.D.O. HAMILTON

Axis Genetics Ltd, Babraham, Cambridge CB2 4AZ, UK

ABSTRACT

The worldwide output from agriculture is unable to meet the global demands for food today. Not only is the current application of agriculture unsustainable, but the demands upon it are continuing to increase at a significant rate. The requirement for improved crop resistance and the impact that biotechnology can have are discussed with specific reference to the use of plant-derived pest control genes, their specificity of action and their durability. The major beneficiaries of this technology should be the less-developed countries but the application of biotechnology in such regions is not straightforward. A number of these problems are considered.

INTRODUCTION

Biotechnology encompasses a wide range of techniques, of varying degrees of sophistication, which may be of value in increasing the resistance of crops to pests, pathogens, weeds and biotic stresses. This paper is confined to discussion of those involving the introduction of *foreign* genes into crop plants -- the genetic engineering of resistance -- and will concentrate in particular on resistance to pests. However, the potential for biotechnology to enhance other forms of resistance and other agronomic characters will be of similar significance to the agriculture of the future.

THE NEED FOR IMPROVED CROP RESISTANCE

Worldwide agricultural output is unable to meet even the most basic needs of a sizeable fraction of humanity, with around one billion people suffering from hunger or malnutrition today. In 18 countries of sub-Saharan Africa it has been estimated that 45% of the population lives in absolute poverty; in 12 of these countries the figure is above 65% (Myers *et al.*, 1985). This problem is exacerbated by the rate at which growth of the human population is outstripping improvements in agricultural productivity. In some less-developed countries this is not a matter of mere statistics, but of life and death itself. But even the high-unit-output agricultural systems of the developed world are coming under increasing pressure due to their heavy dependence on high levels of industrial inputs. The view is now widely held that such systems are unsustainable because of their huge cost in terms of non-renewable resources; their inefficiency in terms of the proportion of these resources which actually miss their intended target; the environmentally unacceptable consequences of the preceding criticisms, such as contamination of food chains and water sources and physical degradation of the environment; and growing consumer dissatisfaction with the publicly perceived consequences of high-input agricultural practices.

We are faced, therefore, with the dilemma of accomplishing a massive increase in food production, by an estimated 75% by the year 2000 (Blaxter, 1986), but doing so in a sustainable, environmentally friendly way. A substantial contribution to this end could be made by preserving more of what is grown for its intended end use. It is estimated that approximately 40% of agricultural production is lost to pests, pathogens and weeds; this despite the current approximately US$27 billion spent annually on crop protection. There is clearly scope for improvement here, and increasing the inherent resistance of crop plants is an obvious target -- indeed, one which has been a major goal for many conventional plant breeding programmes for years and one of the earliest identified objectives of plant genetic engineering.

Crop losses due to insect pests are crudely estimated at around 14% of potential global yield (range for specific crop per area = 0-100%), despite the expenditure of some approximately US$8 billion per year on synthetic chemical insecticides. Crops with inherent insect resistance have the potential to offer a huge saving in production costs, substituting for some of the expenditure on insecticides, and to enable huge savings in yield.

Similarly, nematodes are pests of major economic importance worldwide, but are of particular importance in the tropical and sub-tropical regions where they may be a major constraint on agriculture. For example, losses due to parasitic nematodes on bananas and plantains have been estimated as varying from 5-263% (over several crop cycles) and the progressive decline of ratoon crops may necessitate replanting within 5 years (Gowen and Queneherve, 1990). There are at present few effective, acceptable options for nematode control. Development of more nematode-resistant crops would allow the substitution of the highly toxic chemical nematicides currently in use and permit cultivation where farmers could not previously afford or justify nematode control.

Securing anything like an adequate world food supply in the future will depend on the development of sustainable agricultural systems which will not be dependent on high inputs of non-renewable resources. The technical advantages of using cultivars with high inherent resistance, relative to the use of exogenously applied chemical protectants, have been outlined before (*eg.* Boulter, 1993a). Many modern, high-yielding cultivars are considerably less resistant than their wild relatives. Enhancing inherent resistance by genetic engineering might offer new solutions to some of these problems of crop protection.

WHAT CAN BIOTECHNOLOGY DO?

Genetic engineering offers a number of unique benefits over conventional plant breeding for resistance. It widens the potential gene pool from which *resistance* genes may be taken, as genes from any source, not just interbreeding plants, may be selected for transfer. It allows a number of different desirable genes, from different sources, to be introduced in a single event into a crop species, and reduces the time required to introgress introduced desirable characters into an elite genetic background.

The practical application of plant genetic engineering involves two equally important constituents, cellular and molecular biology. The list of crop species which are amenable to genetic engineering has grown steadily and now includes some of the major grain monocots, such as rice, maize and wheat, and some of the legumes, such as soyabean and pea, which were previously recalcitrant. Transforming many of the most important crop species remains, however, a far from trivial exercise and is frequently genotype-dependent, with elite lines usually proving harder to transform than model varieties. Many of these transformable crops are of major importance in the developing world, but there remain many *orphan* crops for which transformation systems have not been successfully developed. The development of transformation systems for these orphan crops should be a priority funding target area for the international aid agencies. Transformation technology continues to be developed at a rapid pace and recent advances have been made using established technology, *eg.* the use of *Agrobacterium tumefaciens* to transform rice at high efficiency (Hiei *et al.*, 1994) as well as the development of new technologies, *eg.* silicon carbide fibre-mediated DNA delivery (Kaeppler *et al.*, 1990; Wilson *et al.*, 1994). These two developments demonstrate that transformation of such *orphan* crops should be possible in the future, and that methodologies should become available that do not depend on expensive equipment or consumables.

The list of genes which might usefully be transferred into transgenic crops has not grown at a similar pace, although there are now a number of genes which confer enhanced resistance to various yield-limiting agents. By far the greatest research effort in developing pest-resistant transgenic crops has gone into expression of *Bacillus thuringiensis* (*Bt*) toxins in plants.

Transgenic crops expressing *Bt* toxins

The crystal toxin genes produced by the insect pathogenic bacterium *Bacillus thuringiensis* have been in limited field use as biological control agents for more than 25 years. Expression of modified genes encoding the *Bt* toxin provided the first examples of genetically engineered insect resistance in plants (Barton *et al.*, 1987; Fischhoff *et al.*, 1987; Vaeck *et al.*, 1987). *Bt* toxins are very effective in controlling neonate larvae of susceptible lepidopteran insect species, but the range of pest species which are susceptible to any particular *Bt* toxin is extremely limited. In order to obtain adequate levels of expression in plants of this bacterial gene it has had to be substantially modified -- truncated, altered in codon usage and fused to highly efficient promoters -- to the extent that the current generation of *Bt* toxin genes are essentially 'rebuilt' (Perlak *et al.*, 1991). *Bt* toxin has now been expressed in such major crops as cotton (Perlak *et al.*, 1990), maize (Koziel *et al.*, 1993) and rice (Fujimoto *et al.*, 1993), with the transgenics showing good resistance to the major lepidopteran pests in both laboratory and field trials. Commercialisation of the first of these genetically modified, insect resistant crops is expected within the present decade.

Transgenic crops expressing plant-derived pest control proteins

An alternative source of pest control genes are plants themselves: exploiting the plants' solutions to the plants' problems in a *copy nature* strategy (Boulter, 1993b). Within the Axis Genetics Ltd/Durham University Insect Resistance Programme, a number of quite different types of plant protein have been identified which have pest control properties, including enzymes, enzyme inhibitors and lectins. Work is in progress with over a dozen different plant-derived genes, representing more than six different classes of pest control protein (reviewed by Gatehouse *et al.*, 1992; Hilder *et al.*, 1992).

The paradigm of this approach is cowpea trypsin inhibitor (CpTI), expression of which in the leaves of transgenic plants enhances their resistance to various lepidopteran pests

(Hilder *et al.*, 1987). Such limited field trial data as is available suggests that a similar level of partial control is achieved in the field (Hoffmann *et al.*, 1992). There are unpublished reports of successful field trials of CpTI-expressing transgenics in China.

CpTI serves to illustrate two important general characteristics of these plant-derived pest control proteins. (1) Their absolute toxicity is relatively low, especially compared with synthetic pesticides or *Bt* toxins. They rarely produce 100% kill of insects in any realistic trial, tending rather to increase mortality to a limited extent but significantly to retard insect development and growth. (2) They tend to have an effect against a broad spectrum of pests (Table 1). Thus CpTI has been demonstrated to have some significant effect not only against a number of pest species of lepidopteran and coleopteran insects, but also against some orthopterans (Good *et al.*, 1994) and plant-parasitic nematodes (Atkinson, 1993). Similarly, the mannose-specific lectin from snowdrops (GNA) is effective not only against lepidopterans and coleopterans, but expression of GNA in transgenic plants offers the potential to control the sap-sucking homopteran insects (Hilder *et al.*, 1994), a very important group of pests.

TABLE 1. Spectrum of activity of pest control proteins.

	Protease inhibitors		Lectins		Chitinase	*Bt* toxins	
	Serine	Thiol	Mannose	NAcGlu		cryI	cryIII
Lepidopteran	+	-	+	+	+	+	-
Coleopteran	+	+	+	+		-	+
Homopteran	-		+	+	-	-	-
Nematodes	+	+	+				
Fungi			+	+	+	-	-
Mammals	±	-	-	+	-	-	-

SPECIFICITY OF ACTION

Different considerations apply to the spectrum of activity of transgenic plants expressing pest control proteins than to synthetic, exogenously applied pesticides. The aim with transgenic plants should be to provide a broad spectrum of protection, whereas there is a trend to favour highly selective, narrow-spectrum pesticides. Because the transgene products are essentially confined within the host plant, they are intrinsically specific to those pests which are heinous enough to invade and eat the crop. It should be remembered that most crops are not subject to attack by a single pest species but by an entire complex of different pests. For example, the cowpea crop in Africa is vulnerable to attack by a range of insects throughout the growing season until post-harvest storage. Major pests belong to the orders homoptera, lepidoptera, coleoptera and thysanoptera, with any single species capable of reducing yield by 20-100% (IITA, 1984). Similarly cotton, although grown under a number of different cropping systems, is subject to losses to a surprisingly similar pest complex worldwide, principally heliothines, mirids, aphids, spider mites and thrips (Lutterell *et al.*, 1994). The advantage of, say, transgenic cotton with protection against boll worms would be seriously limited if it were still necessary to make a dozen applications of insecticide to control other members of the pest complex.

Within a transgenic plant, the broader the spectrum of activity against different pests the better. From the farmer's point of view, what ultimately matters is not how many dead individuals of a particular pest species there are, but what is the yield in the face of the challenge from the whole pest complex.

It is, of course, important that intended consumers of the transgenic crop are not included within the spectrum of activity. Many insecticidal plant-derived proteins are notoriously toxic to humans (eg. the lectins wheat germ agglutinin and *Phaseolus* bean agglutinin). This has to be a major concern in the selection of genes; proteins such as CpTI and GNA have been demonstrated to be benign in independent mammalian feeding trials (Puzstai *et al.*, 1990; 1992). Further work is needed to clarify their possible effects on beneficial insects in insect-pollinated crops.

Arguments for broad-spectrum activity may also apply to where and when in the plant the protein is expressed. There appears to be little reason to restrict the activity of broad-spectrum pest control proteins within the plant by the use of tissue-specific, developmentally regulated or inducible promoters. It has been suggested that such regulated expression would minimise any yield penalty associated with transgene expression, but all the available evidence from laboratory trials (Hilder and Gatehouse, 1991) and field trials (Table 2) suggests that there is no such penalty to minimise. It has also been suggested that restricting expression in the plant could contribute to management of resistance build-up in the pest, although it unclear how this is supposed to work. There are some cases where specific promoters might be advantageous, eg. for root-feeding nematodes which modify expression at the feeding sites and tend to inactivate general promoters.

DURABILITY OF RESISTANCE

The development of resistance to *Bt* toxins in the laboratory and the field has set alarm bells ringing in many quarters (McGaughey and Whalon, 1992; Tabashnik, 1994). This is particularly acute due to the position of *Bt* as the leading bio-insecticide, and the toxin's high kill rate leading to high selective pressure for resistant insects. Both of these should prove less severe problems with the types of plant-derived proteins described above. Various resistance management strategies have been proposed, of which the use of more than a single resistance factor, and the provision of refugia to ensure survival of susceptible genotypes, appear to be of most value. The ability of pests to break down host-plant resistance is always a grave risk where single factor resistance is involved. The durability of transgenic crops is likely to be much higher if they are deployed with multigene, multimechanistic resistance within them (Boulter, 1993b). One demonstration of *pyramiding* different resistance mechanisms in transgenic plants has been described (Boulter *et al.*, 1990). Much of the argument concerning resistance management is based on mathematical models and laboratory studies, rather than on experience in the field. Determination of the optimum strategies for deploying transgenics in specific cropping systems must be a key area for future research.

TABLE 2.   Field performance of transgenic plants expressing resistance genes in the absence of challenge.

Crop	Gene	Expression	Yield	Reference
Tomato	TMV-CP	0.02%	=CON	Nelson *et al.*, 1988
Tobacco	*bar*	0.01%	=CON	De Greef *et al.*, 1989
		0.1%	=CON	
Potato	*bar*	0.01%	=CON	De Greef *et al.*, 1989
		0.1%	=CON	
Potato	PVX-CP	0.005%	=CON	Kaniewski *et al.*, 1990
	+PVY-CP	0.01%	=CON	
Flax	*als*	N/A	=CON	McHughen & Holm, 1991
Oilseed rape	*bar*	N/A	=CON	Crawley *et al.*, 1993

=CON, no significant difference from untransformed controls.

INTEGRATED PEST MANAGEMENT

It is frequently stated that transgenic crops with enhanced resistance will be used within integrated pest management (IPM) programmes, the acronym sometimes appearing as a talisman to ward off any remaining criticism of the technology. Would resistant plants of the type discussed above actually be of benefit to IPM? Many IPM practices, such as the use of short-season varieties and conservation of predators, are aimed at preventing the build-up of pest populations to catastrophic levels, rather than total elimination of the pest. Retardation of development, leading to a slower rate of population build-up, and the relative weakness of surviving pests should mean that even in those situations where transgene expression did not keep the pest population below the threshold for intervention, it should allow a much wider window within which intervention can be successfully employed. This might encourage greater confidence in the IPM approach on the part of farmers.

BIOTECHNOLOGY AND THE DEVELOPING WORLD

Most biotechnology research for agriculture is taking place in the developed world, with a very large part of it occurring in the commercial sector. To date, more than 74% of transgenic plant field trials have been carried out by 60 private companies worldwide (Ahl Goy *et al.*, 1994). This research effort is largely driven by the problems in high-input agricultural systems of the developed world, with an eye on the huge agrochemical markets. However, most of the developments to date are applicable to general agricultural problems. As these problems often pose a greater constraint to agricultural output in less-developed countries than in developed ones, the benefits of any solutions are likely to be of even greater significance to the former. Whereas relatively high degrees of resistance are sought in the engineering of crops for the developed world, consultation with the UK Overseas Development Administration (ODA) suggests that in a number of cases, engineering an increase in resistance of just a few percent would make a huge difference to productivity in the less-developed countries.

The location of much of the research effort in the commercial sector of developed countries has led to various spectres being raised concerning restrictions on the transfer of this technology to less-developed countries. It should be pointed out that several companies have entered into agreements whereby their proprietary technology can be used royalty-free in less-developed countries. Walgate (1990) has suggested a number of reasons why the commercial sector would be willing, in fact, to transfer its proprietary technology to the developing world. However, it is sad that he does not consider the possibility that those involved would seriously like to see this technology employed to assist less-developed countries out of common humanity. It should be remembered that there are very few agricultural systems in the less-developed countries from which companies could recover a significant fraction of the development costs for their proprietary technology.

In addition to inherent difficulties with the cellular and molecular biology involved in the production of engineered crops, there are a number of other factors that could limit the application of this technology in less-developed countries. These include, in particular: (1) The inherently high cost of this technology. Biotechnology is not cheap and the cost of applying it to locally grown varieties would probably have to be borne by the less-developed country or by aid agencies. (2) The necessity to devise and implement adequate biosafety regulatory procedures and legislation. It is essential that full consideration is given to these issues before the production of material for field testing.

APPROPRIATE TECHNOLOGY

Genetically engineered crops are intrinsically *user-friendly*. The goals of biotechnology are essentially the same as those of traditional plant breeding, *i.e.* the provision of improved crop varieties that require the minimum input of non-renewable resources to give a consistent, improved yield. As such they are appropriate to any agricultural system. The use of genetically engineered seeds would require no additional inputs or technical skills from farmers -- indeed no other change in farming practice is necessary. They are applicable to any scale of agriculture and would not favour large-scale farmers. The availability of transgenic seeds should simply afford the farmer a greater choice.

CONCLUSIONS

There is clear potential for genetically engineered crops with enhanced resistance to have a significant impact on agricultural systems in both the developed and developing worlds. The application of such technology offers the advantages of being environmentally friendly, user friendly and consumer friendly. The development of this technology has depended on an expensive and sophisticated research effort, much of which has been carried out in the commercial sector. There is little doubt that the technology is becoming ripe for transfer to less-developed countries where it might have the most beneficial impact on agricultural production.

ACKNOWLEDGEMENTS

The authors are grateful to many colleagues for discussions which have been helpful in the development of these ideas; especially to Don Boulter and Iain Cubitt. Funding of original research by Axis Genetics Ltd is gratefully acknowledged.

REFERENCES

Ahl Goy, P.; Chasseray, E.; Duessing, J. (1994) Field trials of transgenic plants: an overview. *Agro Food Industry hi tech* **5**, 10-15.

Atkinson, H.J. (1993) Opportunities for improved control of plant parasitic nematodes via plant biotechnology. In: *Opportunities for Molecular Biology in Crop Production,* D.J. Beadle, D.H.L. Bishop, L.G. Copping, G.K. Dixon, and D.W. Hollomon (Eds), Farnham, UK: BCPC.

Barton, K.; Whiteley, H.; Yang, N.-S. (1987) *Bacillus thuringiensis* d–endotoxin in transgenic *Nicotiana tabacum* provides resistance to lepidopteran insects. *Plant Physiology* **85**, 1103–1109.

Blaxter, K.L. (1986) *People, Food and Resources.* Cambridge: Cambridge University Press.

Boulter, D. (1993a) Overcoming the onset of pest resistance with engineered crops. In: *Opportunities for Molecular Biology in Crop Production*, D.J. Beadle, D.H.L. Bishop, L.G. Copping, G.K. Dixon, and D.W. Hollomon (Eds), Farnham, UK: BCPC.

Boulter, D. (1993b) Insect pest control by copying nature using genetically engineered crops. *Phytochemistry* **34**, 1453-1466.

Boulter, D.; Edwards, G.A.; Gatehouse, A.M.R.; Gatehouse, J.A.; Hilder, V.A. (1990) Additive protective effects of incorporating two different higher plant derived insect resistance genes in transgenic tobacco plants. *Crop Protection* **9**, 351-354.

Crawley, M.S.; Hails, R.S.; Rees, M.; Kohn, D.; Buxton S. (1993) Ecology of transgenic oilseed rape in natural habitats. *Nature* **363**, 620-623.

De Greef, W.; Delon, R.; De Block, M.; Leemans, J.; Botterman, J. (1989) Evaluation of herbicide resistance in transgenic crops under field conditions. *Bio/Technology* **7**, 61-64.

Fischhoff, D.A.; Bowdish, K.S.; Perlak, F.J.; Marrone, P.G.; McCormick, S.M.; Niedermeyer, J.G.; Dean, D.A.; Kusano–Kretzmer, K.; Mayer, E.J.; Rochester, D.E.; Rogers, S.G.; Fraley, R.T. (1987) Insect tolerant transgenic tomato plants. *Bio/Technology* **5**, 807-813.

Fujimoto, H.; Itoh, K.; Yamamoto, M.; Kyozuka, J.; Shimamoto, K. (1993) Insect resistant rice generated by introduction of a modified d-endotoxin gene of *Bacillus thuringiensis*. *Bio/Technology* **11**, 1151-1155.

Gatehouse, A.M.R.; Hilder, V.A.; Boulter, D. (1992) Potential of plant-derived genes in the genetic manipulation of crops for insect resistance. In: *Plant Genetic Manipulation for Crop Protection*, A.M.R. Gatehouse, V.A. Hilder and D. Boulter (Eds.), Wallingford, UK: CAB International.

Good, A.; Hare, P.; Anstee, J.H.; Hilder, V.A.; Gatehouse, A.M.R. (1994) Insecticidal properties of cowpea protease inhibitor on *Locusta migratoria*. *Trends in Agricultural Science* (in press).

Gowen, S.; Queneherve, P. (1990) Nematode parasites of bananas, plantains and abaca. In *Plant Parasitic Nematodes in Subtropical and Tropical Agriculture,* M. Luc, R.A. Sikora, J. Bridge (Eds.), Wallingford, UK: CAB International.

Hiei, Y.; Ohta, S.; Komari, T.; Kumashiro, T. (1994) Efficient transformation of rice (*Oryza sativa* L.) mediated by *Agrobacterium*. In: *Abstracts VIIIth International Congress of Plant Tissue and Cell Culture*, Firenze, Italy, June 12-17 1994, p.158.

Hilder, V.A.; Gatehouse, A.M.R. (1991) Phenotypic cost to plants of an extra gene. *Transgenic Research* 1, 54-60.

Hilder, V.A.; Gatehouse, A.M.R.; Sheerman, S.E.; Barker, R.F.; Boulter, D. (1987) A novel mechanism of insect resistance engineered into tobacco. *Nature* 330, 160-163.

Hilder, V.A.; Brough, C.; Gatehouse, A.M.R.; Gatehouse, L.N.; Powell, K.S.; Shi, Y.; Hamilton, W.D.O. (1992) Genes for protecting transgenic crops from chewing and sap-sucking insect pests. In: *1992 British Crop Protection Conference - Pests and Diseases*, 2, 731-740.

Hilder, V.A.; Powell, K.S.; Gatehouse, A.M.R.; Gatehouse, J.A.; Gatehouse, L.N.; Shi, Y.; Hamilton, W.D.O.; Merryweather, A.; Newell, C.A.; Timans, J.C.; Peumans, W.J.; Van Damme, E.; Boulter, D. (1994) Expression of snowdrop lectin in transgenic tobacco plants results in added protection against aphids. *Transgenic Research* (in press).

Hoffmann, M.P.; Zalom, F.G.; Wilson, L.T.; Smilanick, J.M.; Malyj, L.D.; Kiser, J.; Hilder, V.A.; Barnes, W.M. (1992). Field evaluation of transgenic tobacco containing genes encoding *Bacillus thuringiensis* d-endotoxin or cowpea trypsin inhibitor: efficacy against *Helicoverpa zea* (Lepidoptera: Noctuidae). *Journal of Economic Entomology* 85, 2516-2522.

IITA (1984). *Varietal improvement of cowpea*. Ibadan, Nigeria: International Institute of Tropical Agriculture.

Kaeppler, H.F.; Gu, W.; Somers, D.A.; Rines, H.W.; Cockburn, A.F. (1990) Silicon carbide fibre-mediated DNA delivery into plant cells. *Plant Cell Reports* 9, 415-418.

Kaniewski, W.; Larson, C.; Sammons, B.; Haley, L.; Hart, J.; Delannay, X.; Tumer, N.E. (1990) Field resistance of transgenic Russet Burbank potato to effects of infection by potato virus X and potato virus Y. *Bio/Technology* 8, 750-754.

Koziel, M.G.; Beland, G.L.; Bowman, C.; Carozzi, N.B.; Crenshaw, R.; Crossland, L.; Dawson, J.; Desai, N.; Hill, M.; Kadwell, S.; Launis, K.; Lewis, K.; Maddox, D.; McPherson, K.; Meghji, M.R.; Merlin, E.; Rhodes, R.; Warren, G.W.; Wright, M.; Evola, S.V. (1993) Field performance of elite transgenic maize plants expressing an insecticidal protein derived from *Bacillus thuringiensis*. *Bio/Technology* 11, 194-200.

Lutterell, R.G.; Fitt, G.P.; Ramalho, F.S.; Sugonyaev, E.S. (1994) Cotton pest management: A worldwide perspective. *Annual Review of Entomology* 39, 517-526.

McGaughey, W.H.; Whalon, M.E. (1992) Managing insect resistance to *Bacillus thuringiensis* toxins. *Science* 258, 1451-1455.

McHughen, A.; Holm, F. (1991) Herbicide resistant transgenic flax field test; agronomic performance in normal and sulfonylurea-containing soils. *Euphytica* 55, 49-56.

Myers, N. (1985) *The Gaia Atlas of Planet Management*. London: Pan Books.

Nelson, R.S.; McCormick, S.M.; Delannay, X.; Dube, P.; Layton, J.; Anderson, E.J.; Kaniewski, M.; Prakash, R.K.; Horsch, R.B.; Rogers, S.G.; Fraley, R.T.; Beachy, R.N. (1988) Virus tolerance, plant growth, and field performance of transgenic tomato plants expressing coat protein from tobacco mosaic virus. *Bio/Technology* **6**, 403-409.

Perlak, F.J.; Deaton, R.W.; Armstrong, T.A.; Fuchs, R.L.; Sims, S.R.; Greenplate, J.T.; Fischhoff, D.A. (1990) Insect resistant cotton plants. *Bio/Technology* **8**, 939–943.

Perlak, F.J.; Fuchs, R.L.; Dean, D.A.; McPherson, S.L.; Fischhoff, D.A. (1991) Modification of the coding sequence enhances plant expression of insect control protein genes. *Proceedings of the National Academy of Sciences USA* **88**, 3324-3328.

Puzstai, A.; Ewen, S.W.B.; Grant, G.; Peumans, W.J.; Van Damme, E.J.M.; Rubio, L.; Bardocz, S. (1990) Relationship between survival and binding of plant lectins during small intestinal passage and their effectiveness as growth factors. *Digestion* **46**, 308-316.

Pusztai, A.; Grant, G.; Bardoz, S.; Brown, D.J.; Stewart, J.C.; Ewen, S.W.B.; Gatehouse, A.M.R.; Hilder, V.A. (1992) Nutritional evaluation of the trypsin inhibitor from cowpea. *British Journal of Nutrition* **68**, 783-791.

Tabashnik, B.E. (1994) Evolution of resistance to *Bacillus thuringiensis*. *Annual Review of Entomology* **39**, 47-79.

Vaeck, M.; Reynaerts, A.; Hofte, H.; Jansens, S.; DeBeuckeleer, M.; Dean, C.; Zabeau, M.; Van Montagu, M.; Leemans, J. (1987) Transgenic plants protected from insect attack. *Nature* **327**, 33–37.

Walgate R. (1990) Miracle or Menace. *Biotechnology and the Third World*. London: Panas Institute.

Wilson, H.M.; Frame, B.R.; Drayton, P.R.; Bagnall, S.V.; Lewnau, C.J.; Bullock, W.P.; Dunwell, J.M.; Thompson, J.A.; Wang, K. (1994) Production of fertile transgenic maize plants by silicon carbide fibre-mediated transformation. In: *Abstracts VIIIth International Congress of Plant Tissue and Cell Culture*, p.141, Firenze Italy, 12-17 1994.

Session 3

Role and responsibilities
of the public sector

CHANGES IN CROP PROTECTION STRATEGIES FOR LESS-DEVELOPED COUNTRIES: AN ODA PERSPECTIVE

R.W. SMITH

Overseas Development Adminstration, 94 Victoria Street, London SW1E 5JL, UK

ABSTRACT

The author argues that the sustainability of smallholder production systems in less-developed countries depends not only on environmental issues but also on the social and economic requirements of the farmers. It is also argued that low input-low output systems will not alleviate poverty or contribute to economic development. There is a changing role for crop protection, having moved from chemical control alone to fully integrated pest management, which is reflected in the ODA's revised Renewable Natural Resources Strategy. A specific goal and clear objectives for crop protection research have been established for six broad natural resources production systems focused on target countries. Target institutions and the ultimate beneficiaries of the research have been identified.

INTRODUCTION - THE POLICY ENVIRONMENT

The world's land- and water-based resources are in many cases, particularly in the terrestrial environment, already fully or over-exploited. Increasing numbers of people have to be fed from these already depleted resources. In order to achieve this, it has been estimated that agricultural production will have to more than double by the year 2025, particularly in less-developed countries of sub-Saharan Africa and South Asia (Hazell, 1994). To avoid further degradation of our natural resources, productivity must be enhanced on a sustainable basis. This is one of several objectives of the UK Overseas Development Administration (Foreign and Commonwealth Office/ODA, 1994):

- To promote economic reforms

- To enhance productive capacity

- To promote good government

- To undertake direct poverty reduction activities and programmes

- To promote human development, including better education and health, and children by choice

- To promote the status of women

- To help developing countries tackle environmental problems

The objective on which ODA's current research strategy primarily focuses is "to enhance productive capacity" (Tarbit, 1994). The purpose of ODA's strategy is consequently to enhance the productive potential of natural resource production systems in an economically and environmentally sustainable manner (Table 1). To achieve this end, it will be necessary to ensure that outputs are not simply maintained, but optimised.

TABLE 1. ODA's revised Renewable Natural Resources (RNR) Research Strategy: Hierachy of generic objectives

Goal Poverty reduced, economic growth and reform promoted, national environmental problems mitigated		
Purpose Productive capacity in RNR sector enhanced on an economically and environmentally sustainable basis	*Goal* Productive capacity in the RNR sector enhanced on an economically and environmentally sustainable basis	
Outputs Researchable constraints removed	*Purpose* Researchable constraints removed	*Goal* Researchable constraints removed
Activities Research products packaged and their uptake promoted	*Outputs* Research products packaged and their uptake promoted	*Purpose* Research products packaged and their uptake promoted
	Activities Research results created and adapted: promotion pathways established	*Outputs* Research results created and adapted: promotion pathways established
		Activities Research studies, surveys experiments, etc. designed and implemented and promotion pathways identified
RNR RESEARCH STRATEGY LEVEL	**RESEARCH PROGRAMME LEVEL**	**RESEARCH PROJECT LEVEL**
Management responsibility Development agents, target institution	*Management responsibility* Natural Resources Research Department (ODA), delegated to Research Programme Managers	*Management responsibility* Research project managers

Levels of productivity can be raised by sustainable measures such as improving the genetic potential of crops and animals, and realising that potential through developing production systems with the appropriate use of inputs, and the optimal exploitation of natural biological systems. Productivity can also be improved by enhancing the efficiency of post-harvest processing and marketing structures, and by reducing crop and/or product losses caused by pests and diseases.

Recent environmental, economic and social policies of ODA and other aid agencies in favour of sustainability may have contributed to a reduction in productivity. In many less-developed countries, inputs such as agrochemicals (pesticides and fertilisers) and the means for mechanisation have become scarce, mainly due to high costs and to import restrictions imposed in the light of increasing environmental awareness. These policies have not been conducive to the development of internal or export marketing strategies, or to the development of appropriate post-harvest processing and utilisation of surpluses generated at the farm gate. The opportunities for subsistence farmers to become commercial producers have been limited. In many countries small-scale subsistence farmers have been forced to engage in off-farm activities to generate additional income (von Braun and Kennedy, 1994). In addition, falling commodity prices have meant a reduction in income for small-scale farmers engaged in growing commodity crops, either as independent producers or in producer schemes associated with nucleus estates. Many recent examples of participatory rapid rural appraisal studies have revealed that small-scale farmers in most developing countries are concerned about both their own food security and their income earning capacity.

It is the author's opinion that research and development work aimed at supporting subsistence production systems, as opposed to focusing on higher-production alternatives, has tended to sustain poverty rather than alleviate it.

THE DEVELOPMENT OF CROP PROTECTION TECHNOLOGY

Reduction of crop and product losses

Wide levels of crop loss, up to 100% in some instances, are experienced in many crop production systems. Losses may be caused by arthropod pests, fungi, bacteria, viruses, non-cultivable mollicutes, nematodes, rodents, mammals or birds. Historically, the crop protection scientist has sought chemical means of removing or managing the constraints imposed by these pests. There is little need to document the very many success stories, but a few important early examples involving pesticide use are given below.

- Use of herbicides in tropical weed control, including dalapon, atrazine, 2,4-D, 2,4,5-T, paraquat and glyphosate.

- Control of cocoa capsids in Ghana using gamma-BHC.

- Control of cotton bollworms using DDT and carbaryl in Sudan and other African countries.

- Control of locusts with dieldrin.

- Sulphur dusting to control cashew powdery mildew in Tanzania.

- Control of coffee berry disease with copper fungicides.

- Control of Moko disease (banana bacterial wilt) with disinfectants, fumigants and herbicides.

- Control of rice tungro virus with insecticide applications against leaf hopper vectors.

- Nematode control through fumigation of nursery beds and field application of carbofuran.

- Control of rats and other rodents using warfarin and its derivatives.

- Quelea bird control using fenthion.

Large numbers of farmers have used these technologies thereby saving their crops, feeding themselves and their families, and in favourable situations producing surpluses for the local urban markets, for agro-industrial processes and for export. The first generation of pesticides were chemicals which killed the target pest (and often non-target organisms including beneficial ones as well) on contact. They were usually applied at high volume with little regard for either temporal or spatial targeting. Most of the chemical failed to hit the target pests and found its way into the environment at large, killing non-target organisms and causing environmental pollution and exposure risk both to operators and to others living locally. Ecosystem balance was frequently disrupted, leading to an increased need for further interventions (e.g. Zelazny *et al.*, 1985; Guan-Soon, 1990).

Fortunately there have been many scientific advances over the past 50 or so years, including the development of more target-specific and less environmentally damaging chemicals; better formulations and additives; and improved application methods. Chemicals with lower mammalian toxicity have been introduced, application rates have been reduced through the development of low- and ultra-low-volume applicators, and environmental risk reduced through control of droplet size. Targeting has been enhanced using improved application technologies such as sprayers with better nozzles, guards and electrostatic charging of spray droplets. Systemic chemicals, physiologically active substances and hormones have been introduced. A better understanding of the biology of pests has led to scouting and other methods of monitoring pest build-up, which enable the frequency of application to be reduced without loss of efficiency. Tools for monitoring such as the use of pheromones, radar and remote sensing have been developed and epidemiological modelling has led to the identification of economic thresholds which trigger the implementation of a chemical control programme rather than applying to schedule (Zelazny *et al.*, 1987).

The concept of integrated pest management (IPM) has been developed (Stern *et al.*, 1959), within which the need for chemical control has been reduced. Elements of IPM include breeding of pest- and disease-resistant or tolerant crop varieties, the exploitation of biological control using predators and parasites, and the use of agronomic interventions exploiting rotations and combining crops and animals into mixed production systems which discourage the development of pest epidemics. Much research has been done on migratory and wind-borne pests, and the build-up of populations can in some cases (e.g. locusts, armyworms and airborne fungal spores) be predicted using meteorological and population dynamics data, giving early warning for control action to be triggered.

Post-harvest losses due to pests and diseases have been researched and can now be reduced using techniques such as chemical treatments including fumigation; improved storage, packaging, transportation and handling; and in some cases the use of improved varieties and a better understanding of the pre/post-harvest interface.

Research and development opportunities

Despite the advances summarized above, there is no room for complacency: crop losses, particularly in less-developed countries, continue on an unacceptable scale. The reasons for failure sometimes lie in the lack of transfer of technology to the point where it is widely adopted by the farming communities. It may be that the required inputs are not affordable or available at the right time, or that farmers do not have access to the necessary credit facilities. Some of the technologies may not be appropriate to the social and economic environment for which they were intended, as has been shown through farmer participatory approaches and participatory rapid rural appraisals in some countries. There is clearly a need both to address the delivery systems and to continue research into newer and more relevant technologies. There are opportunities and dangers, particularly as science embarks upon the biotechnological revolution based upon advances in molecular biology. Opportunities exist in many crop species to introduce alien genes through transformation technologies from species not related to the crop in question, a situation not possible using traditional breeding methodologies. The dangers of releasing genetically transformed crops have been anticipated, but more research is needed to establish their reality.

As the yield potential of crops and animals increases through genetic improvement and improved management of production systems, and as crop and product losses become reducible to very low levels, the sustainability of production systems is brought into question. It is the author's view that the low-input/low-output systems which have been the basis of all subsistence farming of crops and animals (from the hunter/gatherer systems exploiting the harvesting of natural and wild populations of crops, game and fish, through shifting cultivation, to low input/low output settled smallholder agriculture), are no longer tenable in the face of increasing population pressures and distribution. The world's population needs higher outputs, and for social and economic development, the world's farmers need increased sales and profit margins. The productive potential will continue to increase, but actual productivity will only increase if the systems can be supported by higher levels of inputs than those achieved by maximum sustainable exploitation of the natural environment. Consequently, the welfare of the farmers could be enhanced. Increased levels of input do however remain compatible with the notion of sustainability provided the inputs can be sustained and the resource base not overexploited.

Increasing production and hence the removal of products from the environment will lead to environmental degradation, unless the inputs are optimised to ensure that no environmental degradation occurs in the longer term. This downward spiral can already be seen in, for example, the rice/wheat systems of India, maize systems in Central and Southern Africa, and the irrigated rice systems of East Asia where yields are only being maintained by increasing inputs (Zelazny et al., 1985). A notable exception to this trend has however occurred through the adoption of IPM technologies in Indonesia, where reduction in the use of pesticides has largely restored the ecological balance, the losses caused by rice pests have been reduced through the action of natural enemies, and rice production has been maintained. We have therefore a crop protection model which, if replicated in other natural resource production systems, would contribute to the achievement of sustainable high outputs (Zelazny et al., 1985; Frans, 1993).

The biotechnological revolution will result in improved diagnosis of pests and their variability. Durable resistance to major pests and diseases at the pre- and post-harvest levels will be engineered. Combining such resistance with other aspects of pest management in IPM and integrated agronomic systems will certainly be a way forward. Nevertheless, improving the management of soil, water and crop nutrition within a systems-oriented programme (which includes IPM) is the only way forward to sustainably increased production (Greenland et al., 1994).

CROP PROTECTION IN THE REVISED ODA RESEARCH STRATEGY

ODA produced its first Renewable Natural Resources Research Strategy (RNRRS) in 1989 for implementation from 1990 (ODA, 1990). In the crop protection area priorities were identified for mycology and bacteriology, virology, nematology, entomology and weed science against a crop and commodity background. The five research programme areas were allocated funds and the strategy area was managed as an IPM programme. Priorities for research were identified against commodity profiles and crops within the commodity groups and were addressed within each of these disciplines. The research has resulted in many scientific successes (NRI, 1994) but the uptake of the research results has been questioned, and the consequent impact has been perceived to be less than hoped. In 1993, ODA commissioned an independent review of the RNRRS, and as a result a research task group was constituted to revise the strategy. The task group's final report (Tarbit, 1994) has been accepted and a new 10-year research programme will become effective from April 1995.

The new strategy contributes to the ODA departmental objective of enhancing productive capacity and adopts a production systems approach, focusing on seven production systems (Table 2).

The IPM strategy area is replaced by a Crop Protection strategy area, and has a list of development purposes or objectives relating to only the first six of the production systems in Table 2, as crop protection was not considered important in tropical moist forest systems. The crop protection programme will be required to identify activities and outputs (guided by an indicative list of outputs in the research task group's report). The activities will be strategic and/or adaptive research projects addressing researchable constraints, and delivering outputs which will be packaged and promoted to enhance uptake and impact in less-developed countries. Target institutions, often intermediate users of the research results, are to be identified, as are the ultimate beneficiaries of the research. A summary of the revised strategy will be published in booklet form. The strategy will give a clear indication to UK scientific institutions of what research is to be commissioned and how they will be able to contribute, drawing on their own areas of comparative advantage.

CONCLUSIONS

This brief review attempts to show how crop protection is changing from the early concept of killing all pests by whatever means available, to IPM based on the results of

TABLE 2. ODA production systems and crop protection development purposes.

Production system	Purpose
High potential	1. Yields improved by cost effective reduction in losses due to pests.
Peri-urban interface	1. Volume, quality and seasonal variability of food and crop products improved through the reduction of economic and physical losses caused by pests.
Forest/agriculture interface	1. Yields from cropping systems in tropical moist forest areas increased and their sustainability enhanced by minimising production losses caused by agricultural pests. 2. Sustainability and yield from tree-crop-based systems at the forest/agriculture interface improved through the removal of pest constraints.
Land/water interface	1. Yields from coconut-based farming systems increased through reduction in losses caused by pests. 2. Yields of rice-based systems in floodplain areas increased by application of environmentally benign pest control.
Semi/arid	1. Impact of weeds on the crop production cycle minimised. 2. Impact of significant pests on production from cereal- (particularly sorghum-) based systems minimised. 3. Impact of significant pests of cotton production systems minimised. 4. Impact of migrant pests on crop production minimised.
Hillside	1. Yields from cropping systems on sloping lands optimised and sustainability enhanced by minimising production losses caused by pests. 2. Yields from agroforestry systems on sloping lands optimised and sustainability enhanced by minimising production losses (caused by pests).
Tropical moist forest	(No crop protection purposes)

biological research. IPM, based on sound ecological principles, recognises the need to preserve and enhance the environment in order to retain productive potential for the future.

Sustainable productivity must, however, also recognise social and economic demands. Production must increase very significantly and surpluses be created and marketed at realistic prices to feed increasing populations. The farming business must also be more profitable for farmers if it is to keep them on the land, improve their well being and alleviate the poverty which is associated with all but the larger-scale farmers in less-developed countries. Output must increase, which necessitates an increase of inputs, particularly nutrients, energy and management skills, into production systems.

Science continues to develop component technologies for pest management practices. These technologies are being built into environmentally friendly and socially and economically viable systems which work. The ODA, in its revised RNRRS, will be focusing on a set of priority production systems within which demand-led researchable constraints have been identified. Crop protection continues to be a priority focus for such research, and clients, both intermediate users and end users, have been identified. The uptake of the results of strategic and applied research by these clients will be promoted, and the impact on the ultimate beneficiaries will be monitored.

The future for crop protection in developing countries depends upon the use of IPM approaches within the context of the holistic development of natural resource production systems. Strategic and adaptive research to support development must both respond to demand and need, and react to new emerging opportunities offered by science.

REFERENCES

von Braun, J; Kennedy, E. (Eds) (1994) *Agricultural Commercialization, Economic Development, and Nutrition*. Baltimore: John Hopkins University Press.

Foreign and Commonwealth Office [including Overseas Development Administration] (1994) Departmental Report 1994. London: HMSO Cm 2502.

Frans, R. (1993) Sustainability of high-input cropping systems: the role of IPM. *FAO Plant Protection Bulletin* **41**, 161-170.

Greenland, D.J.; Bowen, G.; Eswaran,H.; Rhoades, R.; Valentin, C. (1994) *Soil, Water and Nutrient Management Research - A New Agenda*, IBSRAM Position Paper. Bangkok, Thailand: International Board for Soil Research and Management.

Guan-Soon, L. (1990) Overview of vegetable IPM in Asia. *FAO Plant Protection Bulletin* **38**, 73-87.

Hazell, P.B.R. (1994) *Rainfed versus Irrigated Areas - Emerging Policy Issues for Agricultural Research*, IFPRI Report **16** No 2, June 1994. Washington, DC: International Food Policy Research Institute.

NRI (1994) Annual Report, IPM Research Programme, 1993. Chatham Maritime: Natural Resources Institute.

ODA (1990) *Renewable Natural Resources Research Strategy*. London: Overseas Development Administration.

Stern, V.M.; Smith, R.F.; Van den Bosch, R.; Hagen, K. (1959) The integrated control concept. *Hilgardia* **29**, 81-101.

Tarbit (1994) Final Report of the Research Task Group. London: Overseas Development Admnistration Internal Report.

Zelazny, B.; Chiarappa, L.; Kenmore, P. (1985) Integrated pest control in developing countries. *FAO Plant Protection Bulletin* **33**, 147-158.

CROP PROTECTION FOR SUBSISTENCE CULTIVATORS: WHAT ARE THE ANSWERS?

SIMON CROXTON

Intermediate Technology Development Group, Myson House, Railway Terrace, Rugby CV21 3HT, UK

ABSTRACT

This paper examines strategies for pest management in low-external-input agricultural systems which are mainly geared towards subsistence production. These systems are widespread in less-developed countries, and are the basis of the food security of a large proportion of the world's population. The paper examines the ways in which integrated pest management (IPM) strategies may or may not be able to balance the costs of pest damage and control with the returns of subsistence agriculture and goals of subsistence farmers. It discusses the concept of technical capacity in relation to pest control strategies and argues for the recognition of the value of local, traditional pest control practices as part of IPM strategies.

INTRODUCTION

The food security of large numbers of small-scale farmers in less-developed countries depends on the crops they can produce from small parcels of land. Typically they are farming in areas in which the physical environment presents great constraints to agricultural production. Frequently the economic and political environment is not particularly supportive of small-scale agricultural production. In this situation, any technology that can assist farmers to produce and sustain better yields and increase the reliability of their cropping, should be utilised as effectively as possible.

Without doubt, pests and diseases are an important cause of the low yields which so frequently characterise these farming systems. Farmers frequently place them at the top of their lists of chronic constraints on agricultural production. Yet while great advances in pest control strategies have been made in the last 30 or 40 years, very few of these practices seem to have been used by large numbers of small-scale farmers in less-developed countries.

Pest control strategies are not the only apparently useful technology that has failed to have an impact on rural communities in the developing world. There is clearly a long way to go before technologies that meet the needs and aspirations of rural communities achieve widespread acceptance. (*Technology* is defined very broadly here to include techniques as well as pieces of equipment.) This has long been recognised and in the past the debate surrounding this issue focused on so-called *appropriate technologies*. The assertion was: if technologies utilising the limited resources that were readily available to rural people could be devised, identified, modified or adapted, then these technologies would stand a far greater chance of being used. Pest control technologies were included in this debate (Letcher, 1990). However, the promised breakthroughs have never occurred. Where there are success stories their impact is often limited to specific areas, or fails to reach the most disadvantaged groups.

More recently the debate has moved away from the nuts and bolts aspects of technologies and shifted towards the approaches used in technology development and dissemination. The result of this has been a critique of the previous *transfer of technology* (TOT) paradigm, where the process was controlled largely by external agents. The move is now towards a more participatory approach, sometimes now referred to as the *farmer first* approach. (This phrase, although in common use, is not ideal as it implies that farmers are the only users of rural technologies.) The farmer first approach puts end-users of a technology in the centre of the picture during the technology development process. It stresses the importance of understanding and building on local peoples' skills and knowledge. It also stresses supporting and strengthening local institutions and traditional organisational structures to manage technological innovations. Very importantly, this approach recognises the importance of building peoples' self-confidence to continue to adapt technologies to meet their needs, as these develop over time. The idea that technologies should be based on rural peoples' resources was not in itself fundamentally flawed, however it is now recognised that the best people to understand both the needs and the resources of rural people are rural people themselves.

Intellectually, the change may be described as moving away from a fixation on particular technical packages and towards an approach that strengthens peoples' *technical capacity* in a broader way -- looking at ways of supporting their abilities to identify, adapt and innovate technology they use or would like to use. It is the *know why* rather than the *know how* of production (Croxton & Appleton, 1994). This concept also includes the organisational capability to manage and use a particular technology.

Farmer participation is part and parcel of this approach. However, as this term can itself mean different things to different people, it may be useful to clarify how it is understood here. There are two main schools of thought concerning the concept and practice of peoples' participation in development. On one side are those who view participation as the necessary inclusion of human resources in development efforts. Here it becomes little more than yet another input into development projects. The second school looks very differently at the concept and sees participation closely linked to tackling structural causes of poverty. It is a process that seeks to increase the influence of disadvantaged groups and so gain access to technologies and other resources that would help to sustain or improve their standard of living (Oakley, 1994). It is this latter understanding of participation that is used by many non-governmental organisations, and is used in this paper.

INTEGRATED PEST MANAGEMENT STRATEGIES

Pest control strategies that rely on chemical controls have been the subject of widespread criticism. It is not the intention of this paper to revisit these arguments, which are articulated clearly elsewhere (e.g. Gips, 1987; Conway & Pretty, 1991). However, the shift of focus towards integrated pest management (IPM) strategies can be regarded as a response to the concerns raised over the various shortcomings of pest control based purely on chemical methods. IPM strategies seek to tackle the problems of pest control in ways that are more suited to sustainable agricultural production. These strategies seek to build upon complementarities between different pest control measures. IPM has five major foci:

- the use of cultural practices such as careful selection of planting and harvesting dates, intercropping, crop rotations, etc.;

- breeding and using plant varieties that are more resistant to pests;

- the selective use of pesticides (chemical, botanical and microbial) combined with information on economic thresholds;

- biological control mechanisms such as conserving natural enemies, manipulating their populations or introducing exotic organisms;

- legal control over issues such as management practices and quarantine.

ARE IPM METHODS APPROPRIATE FOR SMALL-SCALE FARMERS?

IPM strategies do not in themselves break away from the TOT model of technology development and dissemination. In particular, there is not necessarily any compulsion to include farmers in developing an IPM strategy, except as people who are consulted. Neither is there any compulsion to recognise, value or use farmers' own knowledge and experience. In other words, there is no compulsion to let farmers make key decisions in IPM strategies.

Conventional approaches tend to emphasise the values of western scientific thinking. Much of what is done is determined by a particular value system that defines what to think and how to think about it, and informs the choice of what is to be researched. This perspective in turn tends to place certain boundaries around what is included in the research and development of IPM strategies (Pimbert, 1991).

Pest control is not the only area of rural technology where the conventional TOT model has failed to come up with recommendations that are adopted. However, pest control is the focus of this paper, and some of the many problems that have repeatedly occurred are detailed below.

- Chemical controls are too expensive for farmers to use, or are unobtainable. In semi-arid environments, where pest populations vary from year to year and yields are intrinsically low, there may be no realistic economic threshold for poor farmers to use chemical controls.

- Farmers do not plant certain pest-resistant varieties because they do not like their taste, are concerned over storage properties, fail to obtain a good market price, or suffer from a combination of these and other factors.

- Weed control operations create new problems as they also destroy plants that are utilised by key predator species.

Many of these failings can be attributed to the fact that pest problems are identified in isolation from farmers by researchers on research stations. There is no use of farmers' knowledge or of their perceptions.

The alternative, farmer first approach places a higher value on farmers' perceptions, and views the problem very differently, linking to a broader understanding of the structural conditions that affect a farming system, and placing pest control within this wider context. The key differences between a capital-intensive model, the conventional IPM model, and the farmer-centred approach, are illustrated in Table 1.

Proponents of this alternative approach argue that appropriate solutions to pest problems will only be arrived at if farmers themselves are included in their identification and development, and that this takes place in a research environment which permits a more holistic view of the problem to be taken. This is not to argue naively that farmers are always right. It is much more a case of identifying complementarities between western, positivist thinking and traditional knowledge systems. This will allow all involved to look at the problem of pest control in a more holistic fashion. This in turn will result in approaching problem identification and problem solving in a more open way, that values various sources of knowledge.

TRADITIONAL STRATEGIES

Farmers themselves possess a vast repertoire of strategies. Examples of these (from Altieri, 1993) are given below.

- *Mechanical and physical practices*: scarecrows; sound devices; wrapping of fruits and pods; painting stems and trunks with lime or other materials; destroying ant nests, digging out eggs/larvae; hand picking; removal of infested plants; selective pruning; application of materials (ash, salt etc.); burning vegetation.

- *Cultural practices*: intercropping; overplanting or varying seeding rates; changing planting dates; crop rotation; timing of harvest; mixing crop varieties; selective weeding; use of resistant varieties; fertiliser management; water management.

Such techniques are often simple, but frequently effective. A major problem with them may be that, because these techniques are not accorded sufficient scientific status, information concerning the detail of some of these strategies is not disseminated by formal extension services.

It must be remembered that subsistence farmers do not always regard financial returns as the key criterion when selecting crop protection strategies. Labour-intensive methods are not always regarded as a constraint if other goals are met. Indeed, many subsistence cultivators would not give family labour a financial price. Pests may be tolerated because they have other uses (e.g. as medicines, or as other agricultural products).

TABLE 1. Comparison of pest management strategies in different approaches to agricultural development.

	Industrial & Green Revolution	Present IPM (systematic adjustments)	Sustainable agriculture (structural changes)
Goal	Eliminate or reduce pest species	Reduce costs of production	Multiple economic, ecological and social goals
Target	Single pest	Several pests around a crop and their predators	Fauna and flora of a cultivated area and linkages with non-cultivated ecologies
Signal for intervention	Calendar date or presence of pest	Economic threshold	Multiple criteria
Principal method	Pesticide	Prevention by plant breeding and crop timing, careful monitoring, product substitution, insecticide resistance management and multiple interventions	Agroecosystem design to minimize pest outbreaks and mixed strategies, including group action on an area-wide basis to complement pest controls aimed at individual households
Diversity	Low	Low to medium	High
Spatial scale	Single farm	Single farm or small region defined by pest	Biogeographic region
Time scale	Immediate	Single season	Long term steady-state oscillatory dynamics
Boundary conditions	Everything as is: crops, cropping system, land tenure, microeconomic decision rules, social organisation	Major crops, land tenure, and decision rules. Economy treated as given but subject to some intervention via price supports and subsidies	Social goals
Research goal	Improved pesticides	More kinds of interventions	Minimize need for intervention
Research mode	Transfer of technology (TOT)	TOT mode	Complementarity between TOT and farmer first mode (FF)

Source: Pimbert (1991), based on Levins (1986).

Farmers frequently have a sophisticated knowledge of crop pests, their behaviour and the damage they cause (Altieri, 1993). Farmers also adopt cultural practices that seek to manipulate crops and their surrounding ecosystems in terms of space, time and diversity.

WHERE NEXT?

Increasingly, researchers are beginning to include farmers in research on pests (Ashby, 1987; van Schoubroeck *et al.*, 1990; Altieri, 1993). This process invariably results in approaching the problem in a way that utilises principles and techniques that work with and enhance natural biological processes and control mechanisms. If IPM strategies are to be developed that really do serve the needs of small-scale farmers, then this approach should be supported.

Identifying and building on the best of local practice when developing and implementing IPM strategies implies that more emphasis needs to be placed on working with biological processes and agroecological principles, for these are the basis of traditional farming practices. Farming systems that exploit diversity and which are based on agroecological principles, using a minimum of external inputs, are increasingly recognised as being the most suitable systems for small-scale, resource-poor farmers in less-developed countries, rather than adopting green revolution technologies (Altieri, 1987; Reijntjes *et al.*, 1992). Bearing these factors in mind implies that a critical issue is ensuring that IPM strategies are weighted in such a way as to optimise resources internal to the system. Farmers are best placed to identify these resources.

In addition, it is becoming more and more apparent that real progress can be made if the issue of strengthening and supporting technical capacity is addressed in a more general way, rather than focusing on individual problem areas (ITDG, 1993). This provides people with the necessary skills, knowledge and self-confidence (which may well include being able to approach external agents for advice and support) to continue to develop and adapt technologies, for pest control or for other purposes.

IMPLICATIONS FOR EXTERNAL AGENTS

This in turn has major implications for the external agent, whose role changes from that of controller of a process in possession of specialist knowledge, to one of equal partnership with the farmer. The role of the external agent becomes more that of a facilitator who can support farmer experimentation and evaluation, and who is able to provide farmers with information on technology options and assist in the promotion of farmer-to-farmer extension of pest control technology. This approach to pest control, from the perspective of increasing the technical capacity and technology choice of the end-user, has clear implications for the role of outsiders.

- It is important not to begin with a fixed agenda. A process is initiated which begins with users defining problems and then moves towards identifying, testing and evaluating options for possible solutions. Pest control needs to be viewed within the context of farmers' goals -- which are not necessarily the maximisation of yields.

- Problems are defined and solutions identified, tested and evaluated through working with people. Key decisions surrounding these issues are **not** made by outsiders.

- It is important that local skills, knowledge and organisational systems are recognised and built upon from the very beginning of this process.

- If the process leads to a situation where pest control techniques are likely to provide a solution, then the job of scientists and extensionists is to provide a selection of possibilities for users to try.

- The technological capacity of users is an important factor that will determine not only the short-term viability of technical changes, but also the longer-term ability of users to survive successfully in a rapidly changing world.

- The formal education of scientists, extension workers and agricultural planners needs to take account of the demands that are now being made on them, to ensure that new graduates develop the necessary extra skills to enable them to work effectively in wider participative processes.

REFERENCES

Altieri, M.A. (1987) *Agroecology: the Scientific Basis of Alternative Agriculture*. London: Intermediate Technology Publications.

Altieri, M.A. (Ed.) (1993) *Crop Protection Strategies for Subsistence Farmers*. Boulder, Colorado: Westview Press / London: Intermediate Technology Publications.

Ashby, J.; Quiros, C.; Riviera, Y. (1987) *Farmer Participation in On-Farm Trials*. Discussion Paper No. 22, Agricultural Administration Network. London: Overseas Development Institute.

Conway, G.R.; Pretty, J.N. (1991) *Unwelcome Harvest: Agriculture and Pollution*. London: Earthscan.

Croxton, S.P.; Appleton, H.R. (1994) The role of participative approaches in increasing the technical capacity and technology choice of rural communities. In: *Proceedings of a Workshop on Rural Mechanisation, Technology for Rural Livelihoods: Current Issues for Engineers and Social Scientists*, NRI, 6-7 September 1994. Chatham Maritime: Natural Resources Institute (in press).

Gips, T. (1987) *Breaking the Pesticide Habit*. Minnesota, USA: International Alliance for Sustainable Agriculture.

ITDG (1993) *Proceedings of a Workshop on Participatory Technology Development*, Amsterdam, 5-9 December, 1994. Rugby, UK: Intermediate Technology Development Group.

Letcher, M.R. (1990) *Pesticides - Technology Appropriate or Inappropriate to the Needs of the Developing World?* Salford: Environmental Resources Unit, University of Salford.

Levins, R. (1986) Perspectives in integrated pest management: from an industrial to an ecological model of pest management. In: Kogan, M. (Ed.) *Ecological Theory and Pest Management Practice*. London: Wiley.

Oakley, P. (1994) Peoples' participation in rural development: reviewing the balance sheet. Paper presented at Workshop of International NGO Training and Resource Centre (INTRAC), Cambridge, UK, July 1994.

Pimbert, M.P. (1991) *Designing Integrated Pest Management for Sustainable and Productive Futures*. Gatekeeper Series No. 23. London: International Institute for Environment and Development.

Reijntjes, C.; Havercort, B.; Waters-Bayer, A. (1992) *Farming for the Future: an Introduction to Low-External-Input and Sustainable Agriculture*. London: Macmillan.

van Schoubroeck, F.H.J.; Herens, M.; DeLeouw, W.; Louwen, J.M.; Overtown, T. (1990) *Managing Pests and Pesticides in Small-scale Agriculture*. The Netherlands: Centre for Development Work.

Session 4
Role and responsibilities
of the private sector

PROMOTING SAFE AND EFFECTIVE USE OF PESTICIDES IN THE DEVELOPING
WORLD: THE NEED FOR AN INTEGRATED AND CO-ORDINATED APPROACH

Xavier LEDRU
Ciba Plant Protection/Farmer Support Team, Crop Protection Division, BP 7.34, CH 4002,
Basel, Switzerland

Mike THOMAS
Zeneca Agrochemicals, Stewardship and Safety Department, Fernhurst, Haslemere, Surrey
GU27 3JE, UK

Claude PRETOT
GIFAP, avenue Albert Lancaster 79a, 1180 Brussels, Belgium

ABSTRACT

In view of threats to both the continued supply of safe, affordable and sustainable
food to the global community, and the maintenance of a healthy and acceptable
environment, modern technologies (and specifically pesticides) are essential to
production. Despite the introduction in 1985 of the FAO International Code of
Conduct on the Distribution and Use of Pesticides, pesticide control continues to
remain variable across the globe. Governments and others, often due to a lack
of necessary resources, have done little to support the code and its principles.

However, during the past 7-8 years the agrochemical industry has demonstrated
its determination to change. Company stewardship programmes have brought
about considerable changes in pesticide marketing techniques and methodology
which have been very beneficial both to the users and to the environment.
Programmes of education and training in the safe and effective use of pesticides
have also increased in number. Within a 3-year period, the GIFAP Safe Use
Projects in Guatemala, Kenya and Thailand have taken a positive lead in
demonstrating how approaches to pesticide use can be improved through
appropriate stewardship techniques, the reduction of risks and the raising of
levels of understanding relative to modern integrated pest management practices.
The evaluations made after training showed that, in general, children and women
are more receptive and ready to change their behaviour when health and safety
are at stake. As clearly stipulated in article 3.8 of the FAO Code of Conduct,
it is only through concerted and integrated collaborative effort between
governments, international and non-governmental organisations, and the private
sector that the benefits of modern technologies can be won, whilst at the same
time reducing the risks.

INTRODUCTION

Living in the developed world, where basic food needs are largely satisfied and
agricultural policy concentrates on the management of agricultural surpluses, makes it

difficult to talk with credibility about modern high-yield crop production. However we must all learn to take a broader view and face the global reality:

- Currently over 780 million people are undernourished and some 50 million people suffer severe food shortages each year. Two out of three children in the developing world are estimated to be underweight through lack of proper food (World Commission on Environment and Development, 1990).

- If a forecasted future population of 10 billion was fed using 1950s (low-input) crop technology, then we would need to plough 25-30 million square miles (the equivalent of South America, North America and Europe and much of Asia), simply to produce food (Avery, 1994).

- In 1993 world cereal production dropped by 4% to an estimated 1.88 billion tons. In 1994 the cereal output must rise by a minimum of 65 million tons (at least 3%) to avoid world stocks running down to unacceptable levels (World Commission on Environment and Development, 1990).

- Gains in rice productivity over the past 25 years are threatened by continued population growth and loss of crop land. Recent projections by economists of the International Rice Research Institute show that to maintain the current *per capita* consumption, the area of rice production must be more than doubled (Hossain, 1993).

The arguments for high-input agriculture appear to be vital not only for the future well-being and stability of our planet, but for the survival of millions still to be born. Crop protection is an integral part of current food production and must be analysed within the context of modern agriculture and sustainable development. If we are to avoid widespread famine and international turmoil, pesticides, certainly in the short term, must continue to play a critical role in high-yielding crop production until displaced by alternative technologies.

Despite the fact that in many less-developed countries legislation for essential control of pesticides is lacking (over 40% of all nations are without an official approval scheme or procedures governing the use of agrochemicals), the industry has demonstrated its determination to develop and promote safe and effective use of plant protection products.

Company stewardship programmes have brought about considerable improvements in research, manufacturing and marketing. Also, programmes of farmer education and training in the safe and effective use of pesticides have increased. In 1991, the International Group of National Associations of Manufacturers of Agrochemical Products (GIFAP), with the funding support of major agrochemicals companies and the Pesticide Trade Association in Japan (SACI), embarked on a series of Safe Use Projects in Guatemala, Kenya and Thailand. The Safe Use Projects aimed to demonstrate, through the principles of the FAO Code of Conduct (FAO, 1990), that it is possible within a limited period to improve understanding, control and effectiveness of pesticides through a co-ordinated, concerted and well managed effort involving all sectors of the community.

This paper analyses the progress achieved by some of these industry initiatives, and aims to encourage governments and international agencies to become future partners with the agrochemical industry in such collaborative efforts to ensure that the global community can provide a continued supply of safe, sustainable and affordable food, and a healthy and acceptable environment.

IMPLEMENTATION OF THE FAO CODE OF CONDUCT

Despite the introduction in 1985 of the FAO International Code of Conduct, control of pesticides continues to remain highly variable across the globe. On one side, GIFAP members have signed on to the principle of the Code and, during the past 7-8 years, through company stewardship programmes there have been considerable changes in pesticide marketing techniques and methodologies which have been very beneficial, both to users and to the environment. Much more work needs to be done, but already the industry has demonstrated its determination to change.

In company stewardship programmes, we have seen the development of better and more effective controls on manufacturing and formulation, improvements to packaging, labelling and distribution, and the establishment of programmes of waste reduction and management. In addition, programmes of farmer education and training in the safe and effective use of pesticides have also increased. But during the same period, governments have done little in relation to the Code. Many, especially the governments of the less-developed nations, most of which lack the necessary resources, continually make pleas to donor agencies, aid bodies and international non-governmental organisations (NGOs) for funding, in particular to help support and train their people to establish pesticide regulation systems and legislation.

Most major agrochemical companies and GIFAP recognise the difficulties related to the safe and effective use of pesticides in the context of the developing world. It is because of this that dedicated effort and resources have been allocated to enable better understanding of the issues and suitable responses adapted to local conditions.

The correct approach toward Safe Use

Despite some variations between countries it is possible to point out many common aspects regarding the attitudes and behaviour of farmers. The fact that safe use is not spontaneously mentioned as a problem by farmers tends to prove that for many, safe use is a non-issue. This means that simply supplying information on safety is not enough to change attitudes and behaviour. One example of an industry survey in an area of the Dominican Republic typically showed:

- 92% of the surveyed farmers were aware that they should wear protective clothes;

- 80% realised they take a risk when not doing so; but only

- 24% claimed they wore protective clothes when spraying.

Globally, the reasons for such an attitude are:

- Safe use does not lead to direct economic benefits

- Farmers do not always bear the direct costs of unsafe application, e.g. drift to other crops or inhabited areas, or consumers exposed to residues

- Farmers have strong ingrained beliefs (*I have been dealing with pesticides for many years and I'm still feeling well*)

- There is a misconception of risks where inhalation is considered much more dangerous than skin contamination when applying pesticides in field crops

- Lack of inputs: easily affordable and comfortable protective clothing is often not available to the farmer

In some countries, farmer training programmes have had some impact through indirect approaches where safety has been translated into economic terms, through the introduction of protective gear adapted to the climate and pretested with the collaboration of farmers, and through the introduction of new packages which avoid direct contact with the concentrate. In areas where there is a high level of previous experience with pesticide contamination, references to these negative effects are used for farmer motivation.

Application techniques have contributed to the introduction and acceptance of safety. Crop-targeted spraying techniques with reduction of spray volumes and good maintenance of sprayers often trigger farmers' interest as they reduce product losses and increase product performance. The obvious impacts on safety, such as reducing soil contamination due to reduced application volumes, and minimising skin contamination by maintaining sprayers properly to avoid leakage, are often not the most appealing messages to get farmers involved.

Some early lessons learnt

In most less-developed countries the crop protection industry is the major source of extension at the level of the small-scale farmer. Long before the FAO Code of Conduct was established, companies produced media materials (posters, leaflets, etc) and established training modules on safety. However, several questions remain unanswered. How can implementation work in practice when so many well-meaning training programmes have difficulties in changing the behaviour of farmers when using pesticides? How can the industry provide more service in countries where profit margins are already squeezed, without losing competitiveness?

Several ingredients are required. Education specialists and anthropologists agree on proper surveying of target farmers to identify their needs, perceptions, expectations and sources of information and to set a baseline for monitoring impact. Changes in knowledge and attitude can be established through interviews with farmers. Changes in practical behaviour should be assessed through field observations, because claimed practice established through interviews may well differ from real practice: farmers are often aware of what they should do regarding safe use of pesticides and will be inclined to give the "right" answers to the questionnaire.

The participation of farmers in technology and programme development can adapt the technology to farmers' needs, create motivation. develop sense of ownership and ensure the long term sustainability of programme impact. Where farmers are organised (in co-operatives for example), direct training of key farmers will provide results. Where farmers are not organised and are spread over a large area, mass marketing can make the best use of the commercial companies' expertise in promotion. Marketing key aspects of safety through a strategic mix of media can bring about dramatic changes in attitudes and behaviour. For example in Colombia, where an international company started a pilot programme to promote the use of protective clothing among the vegetable farmers of four villages in the province of Cundinamarca, an observation survey performed among 136 trained farmers has shown that the use of gloves during spraying increased from 40 to 76% after the start of the communication campaign.

Everyone benefits in the long term from optimised pesticide management at the small-scale farmer level. But it will only be achieved when government agencies, academia (universities, schools of agriculture), extension services and company representatives are all bringing a consistent and powerful message to their customers.

GIFAP SAFE USE PROJECTS

Objectives and structures

The GIFAP Safe Use Projects were aimed at supporting the principles of the FAO Code of Conduct (FAO, 1990), and were intended to act as blueprints for the future. They focused on meeting the increasing demand for food in the developing world by encouraging the creation of sustainable systems of agriculture, without encroaching on fragile ecosystems. They also supported integrated pest management (IPM) methods, where the techniques of pest control are chosen in the context of the associated environment and the economic significance of pest pressure. Started with a global budget of US$4 million on a 3-year programme (June 1991 to June 1994), these projects have yielded very encouraging results.

Local organisation and auditing
The projects began in 1991 with the appointment of three experienced agronomists in Guatemala, Kenya and Thailand. Initially, many questions had to be asked. What was the situation in the individual markets? What were the problems? How could they be best tackled? All aspects of the markets had to be audited so that starting points could be established; only then was it possible to set critical objectives aimed at major improvements in standards of pesticide understanding and management. The standards served as the basis for education and training, measurement of performance, enforcement and/or recognition and reward.

National government support
If the projects were to succeed, then the committed support of governments would be a critical ingredient of success. In addition to agricultural research and extension, this support included assurance that national legislation could back up the project's aims and objectives in each of the chosen countries.

Project scope
While education and training play a major role, the scope of activities required to achieve success is much broader, encompassing the additional dimensions of regulation,

promotion, problem solving, standards development, measurement, enforcement, rewards, recognition and fund raising.

Training and education

The list of those to be trained ranged from the trainers themselves to virtually everyone involved with pesticides from production to application. Education programmes for groups from schools, colleges and the medical services were also included.

For the projects to bring real benefits to the whole community, a massive communication exercise was needed. This has involved radio, television, discussion groups, the press, and general public awareness campaigns aimed at drawing attention to potential pesticide dangers alongside their community benefits. Training documents and basic messages continually referred to IPM concepts and the need to understand pest pressure and dynamics. The emphasis for all farmers and advisors was to use the best combination of cultural, biological and chemical methods that yield the most cost-effective, environmentally sound and socially acceptable pest management for a given crop situation.

Key achievements

Train the trainers

This programme, including industry, government services, school teachers, doctors and social security staff, was the first critical step in starting the "multiplier effect" process. In Guatemala and Kenya, all staff from agricultural extension and agrochemical companies received a one-week training course, and now offer training to farmers and retailers in the project concepts. In addition, in Guatemala farmer leaders within the Indian communities also received a train-the-trainers course to enable them to instruct and advise their peers in the villages. In Thailand, the Department of Agricultural Extension, using the GIFAP training manual, decided to prioritise Safe Use training for all levels of extension workers, retailers and farmers, to which they committed a budget of US$200,000 p.a. (Table 1).

TABLE 1. Thailand Safe Use Project.
Numbers trained between 1991 and 1994.

Programme	Numbers involved
Trainer training	2,200
Retailer training	623
Farmer training	450,000
Education	253 schools 65,000 students
Medical training	1,300 doctors 600 hospitals

Train the farmers

Farmers and farm workers were given practical training on a range of topics. They were taught to understand labels and how to assess when spraying was necessary; how to store products safely, and how to apply products efficiently and effectively to the required minimum.

The number of farmers trained in the projects has already reached several hundred thousand. Standards are improving, with many now able to understand and identify toxicity, the nature and value of protective clothing, the interpretation of pictograms and treatment of poisoning, etc. The training programme included visits to model farms, and co-operation with farm estates and aid-financed development projects.

Radio
In Kenya, because of the scattered agricultural population and the relatively poor communications network, radio has become a useful tool to ensure that messages on effective management of pests reach a wide audience. A popular half-hour weekly serial on the life and times of a farming family has been designed and sponsored by the Safe Use Project. The serial carries messages on IPM and improved agricultural practices, along with prize-winning competitions to design posters and protective clothing for use in the field. According to the Kenya Broadcasting Corporation it is the most popular programme in their 40-year history, eliciting hundreds of letters each week from Kenyans and from listeners in neighbouring countries.

Schools' programme and women's education
Training those directly involved in cropping is, however, only part of the answer. It is of paramount importance -- especially in those areas where agriculture is a way of life -- to educate children and families on the hazards and importance of safety from an early age. Children form a key link in the chain, particularly in areas where adult literacy is low, as they are often the readers of labels and play an important role in the social conscience of the family.

In Guatemala, where two-thirds of children live in rural areas and actively participate in agricultural practices, the *Scarecrow Programme* has been widely used to educate over 60,000 school children. In Thailand, in addition to a similar schools' programme, GIFAP co-operates with CARE International, an NGO working at field level on personal protection and pesticide safety.

Generally speaking, children and women are more receptive and ready to change their behaviour when health and safety are at stake. In addition to specific training programmes directed at smallholder housewives, the Kenya Safe Use Project organised a contest to design and manufacture suitable protective clothing for women who were involved in spraying activities.

Medical programme
Unfortunately the use of pesticides will always carry some risk, and accidents can and do happen. The projects, therefore, include training on emergency procedures, as well as improved management systems for the infrastructure to respond efficiently to such situations. Doctors, paramedics and other medical staff have been brought up-to-date on methods of diagnosis and treatment of pesticide poisoning. Poison centres have been created or upgraded, and supplies of antidotes have been provided where necessary. In Guatemala, where statistics on chemical poisonings were poorly recorded, epidemiological record forms have been developed and information is now regularly received and analysed by a computer facility

provided by the project. The pesticide/toxicology database INTOX is now operational and used by the San Carlos University Toxicological Information Center in Guatemala City.

Certification of dealers

The projects also aimed at improving the standards of distribution networks and the advice communicated by retailers to end users. All retail operations in the three countries now have at least one trained member of staff, and in most cases the owner is also trained in modern pesticide advisory techniques.

However, certain elements will be difficult or even impossible in the short term to change, such as retailers located in urban zones, or small shops selling other goods alongside pesticides. This is the point where government-enforced guidelines or legislation are needed to back up the voluntary process of improvement. But major improvements are occurring: for example in Thailand the Department of Agriculture recently announced new legislation obliging all retailers to undergo training and accreditation before being permitted to sell pesticides. In Guatemala, AGRIQUIMA, the local pesticide association, with the Ministries of Agriculture, Health and Commerce, has embarked on a retailer certification programme where all dealers, after training, will be required to hold an official certificate if they wish to continue to sell pesticides. Over 100 dealers have already received certification.

Model farm concept

In Thailand, in conjunction with the Department of Agriculture's Pesticide Application Research Team, the Safe Use Project has established a model farm concept where old and unsafe spray methods have been replaced by more efficient and safer activities. For example, with accurate insect monitoring and scouting, the frequency of spraying has been reduced alongside a reduction in spray volumes (Table 2).

TABLE 2. Thailand Safe Use Project. Model improvements in pesticide application.

Spraying system	Sprayer type	
	Traditional boat sprayer	Improved airblast sprayer
Equipment	Pump + 2 hoses, open spray tank	Mounted adjustable Silvan nozzles, self-propelled, closed spray tank
Spray volume (l/ha)	3,125-3,750	625-1,250
Operator hours/ha	6.25	0.31
Application rate (ha/h)	0.48	4.2
Number of operators	3	1

Industry improvement programme

The Safe Use Project provides assistance to manufacturers, formulators, repackers and distributors to enable them to meet the standards as highlighted in the FAO Code of Conduct. The FAO Code, along with national legislation and GIFAP guidelines, has provided the mechanism whereby pesticide companies can be audited for compliance. The audit covers structure and location, storage, packaging and labelling, employee safety, transportation and disposal and is managed by three expert groups. The results of audits have enabled many companies to improve their safety records, and most now conform to acceptable standards internationally.

Waste disposal
During the Safe Use audits, concern was raised over large stocks of unwanted pesticides. In Thailand, the project is currently working with Japanese companies on a new high-temperature waste disposal incinerator, to be completed by the end of 1995. In collaboration with the Pesticide Board in Kenya, a programme to remove and destroy obsolete stocks of pesticides is also under way.

Pesticide legislation
The need to apply and enforce adequate legislation applies as much to the registration and approval schemes as to the control of imports. In Kenya, after consultation with the Safe Use Project, the Kenyan Government is amending its Pest Control Products Act to improve registration procedures in compliance with the FAO Code of Conduct, and has recently recruited more inspectors within the Pest Control Product Board in order to enforce the legislation.

In countries where food exports to developed countries face more and more stringent import regulations on residue limits, full compliance with such limits is the key to many of these countries' economic development. Educating the producer is the only practical response to this issue. Various seminars have been held on maximum residue limits for the Fresh Product Exporters Association of Kenya, under the American-sponsored Kenya Export Development Support Project, and more are to follow. The fresh-fruit companies are also offering to support training programmes for their own staff and their outgrowers.

THE FUTURE

It has only been possible to give a flavour of the multiplicity of activities being carried out in GIFAP's three Safe Use Projects, but the potential to improve the way pesticides are used through appropriate stewardship techniques, and to reduce risks and raise levels of understanding of modern IPM practices, has been clearly demonstrated. There is now a desperate international need to take advantage of the lessons learned in Guatemala, Kenya and Thailand. The task is too large for the agrochemical industry to shoulder the burden alone and, as has been demonstrated in the pilot countries, success is dependent on the involvement and commitment of governments, and all those involved in pesticides, working together for a common cause.

Article 3.8 of the FAO Code of Conduct states that

"concerted efforts should be made by governments and pesticide industries to develop and promote integrated pest management systems, and the use of safe, efficient, cost effective application methods. Public-sector groups and international organisations should actively support such activities" (FAO, 1990).

The GIFAP Safe Use Projects are designed to meet the requirements of sustainable agriculture; they are not contrary to, but complementary to IPM practices. Even if chemical products are considered as the last resort in pest control, they must still be used effectively and safely for the essential protection of people and their environment.

The agrochemical industry is pleased to have been a partner in these three Safe Use Projects. It is also happy to help in the design and implementation of such projects in other less-developed countries. Now is the time for governments, international agencies and supportive NGOs to play a key role in co-operating with the agrochemical industry to ensure that the benefits of such modern technology as pesticides can be obtained in a safe and effective manner. By working together, standards can be raised and technology can be used to the benefit of rural communities world-wide. It is only by such concerted and integrated collaborative effort that the global community can ensure the continued supply of safe, sustainable and affordable food and a healthy, acceptable and secure environment for us all to live in.

REFERENCES

Avery, D.T. (1994) *World Food Production: Saving the Earth's Wildlife with Farm Chemicals*. Presented at the Third European Crop Protection Annual General Meeting, Brussels, June 1994.
FAO (1990) *International Code of Conduct on the Distribution and Use of Pesticides* (amended to include Prior Informed Consent in article 9 as adopted in November 1989). Rome: Food and Agriculture Organisation of the United Nations.
Hossain, M. (1993) *IRRI Annual Report for 1992-93*. Manila, Philippines: International Rice Research Institute.
World Commission on Environment and Development (1990) *Our Common Future*. Oxford: Oxford University Press.

DUE DILIGENCE: THE CHALLENGE TO EXPORTERS IN THE DEVELOPING WORLD

ALAN P. LEGGE

Mack Multiples Division, Transfesa Road, Paddock Wood, Kent TN12 6UT, UK

ABSTRACT

The UK Food Safety Act (1990) requires all food suppliers to exercise *due diligence* to avoid committing offences relating to food safety. The exact requirements of *due diligence* under the Act have yet to be established by Case Law. Nevertheless, Mack Multiples Division has set out a clear policy to assist its suppliers in less-developed countries and to discharge its perceived duties under the Act, which include visits to all suppliers, clear records, clear audit trail, residue testing and the development of integrated crop management systems. The results of this work thus far, if measured by microbiological testing of products consumed whole, such as grapes, plus the residue analysis of items such as melons, bananas, grapes, pineapples, avocados, etc, have shown a complete absence of any residue problems. Mack aims to refine continuously and improve its systems to meet the requirements of both the UK multiple retail outlets and the law, but increasing restrictions on the use of pesticides may lead to a change in the cosmetic characteristics of produce.

INTRODUCTION -- FOOD SAFETY LAW

The UK Food Safety Act 1990 (Anon., 1991a) requires any person who sells food for human consumption to ensure that it complies with food safety requirements - including "not only the probable effect of that food" but "the *probable cumulative* effect of food". If a food supplier were to be charged with an offence under the Act, in his/her defence that supplier would need to prove that all reasonable precautions had been taken and all *due diligence* exercised to avoid the commission of the offence. Conviction under Section 33(i) of the Act carries a maximum of 3 months imprisonment, or a fine not exceeding level 5 on the standard scale. Conviction on indictment under any other section gives liability for imprisonment not exceeding 2 years and a fine, depending which section is infringed, not exceeding £20,000. If the offence was committed with the consent, connivance etc, of an officer of the company, that individual, as well as the company may be punished.

The need for legislation to meet public demands and allay fears was amply demonstrated in the 1989 case of Chilean grapes alleged to be contaminated by cyanide (Anon., 1991b) which caused the immediate withdrawal and destruction of $180 million worth of fresh grapes. With no due diligence system in place, all Chilean grapes were suspect. More recently (Anon., 1992a) we have seen the press and public reaction over the misuse of aldicarb on Irish cucumbers.

This concern is manifested in the UK supermarkets seeking a reduction in the use of crop protection chemicals either in a systematic way (Ridge, 1991) or by a steady pressure for the introduction of Integrated Crop Management Systems (Spriegel, 1993).

A POLICY FOR QUALITY ASSURANCE

In the absence of any significant number of prosecutions under the Act -- in fact the only case of a Section 21 "Due Diligence" defence is still under appeal -- we have to make our own interpretation of the requirements.

This policy is incorporated in the *Mack Quality Assurance Manual* (Legge and Bugler, 1994), and we seek to offer focused technical support to our overseas suppliers, without removing their responsibility for producing the crop using entirely safe practice. Item 2 of the Mack Objectives states that we shall .... "Provide for both Mack customers and suppliers the expertise required in the technical and quality assurance spheres, and to provide continuous feedback between the three partners" (the producer, the importer/distributor, and the retailer). Item 3 requires us to "identify and develop suppliers who can fulfil the requirements of customers in all aspects of their production -- hygiene, social, safety, varieties, systems, packhouses and handling/quality assurance". Item 4 states we must "Continuously monitor and aim to improve all aspects of post-harvest handling and holding". With Item 5 we seek "To ensure technology transfer to our suppliers to enable them to maintain high standards in production, handling, product development and packaging".

FOOD SAFETY POLICY MANAGEMENT

Mack make the following recommendations for management of food safety policy:

- Importers' staff should visit all suppliers in all source countries with especially detailed technical support given to new suppliers in the developing world.

- It is important to carry out detailed annual audits on all volume suppliers, to confirm that hygiene, handling and safety all meet customer requirements, and to confirm as far as is possible that only "approved" pesticides as listed by the responsible Authority in the country of production are used on appropriate crops in the specified rates and manner and that no pesticides which are cited in the current edition of EC Prohibition Directive 79/117/EC (Anon., 1994; Table 1), or in the equivalent UK list of severely restricted pesticides (Anon., 1992b), are proposed for use.

- A brief audit should be carried out on every visit, and all visits are logged in a quality assurance database.

- All packages should be code/lot marked to facilitate a full audit trail, and "Hazard and Critical Control Points Analysis" surveys conducted on each product line.

- Wherever available, suppliers should be encouraged to utilise local analytical laboratories for microbiology tests on water supplies -- both irrigation and packhouse, plus residue testing for both pre- and post-harvest crop protection chemicals. For

TABLE 1. Banned pesticides in the EC Prohibition Directive (79/117/EEC, as amended).
Under the Prohibition Directive, the following susbtances "may be neither placed on the market nor used".

Mercury compounds	Persistent organo-chlorine compounds	Other compounds
Mercuric oxide	Aldrin	Ethylene oxide
Mercurous chloride (calomel)	Chlordane	Nitrofen
Other inorganic mercury compounds	Dieldrin	1,2-dibromoethane
Alkyl mercury compounds	DDT	1,2-dichloroethane
Alkoxyalkyl + aryl mercury compounds	Endrin	Dinoseb, its acetate and salts
	HCH containing < 99% of the gamma isomer	Binapacryl
	Heptachlor	Captafol
	Hexachlorobenzene	*Dicofol containing < 78% of p.p. dicofol or > 1 g/kg DDT and DDT-related compounds
	Camphechlor	*Maleic hydrazide:
		(a) its salts other than its choline, potassium and sodium salts;
		(b) its choline, potassium and sodium salts containing containing > 1 mg/kg free hydrazine expressed on the basis of the acid equivalent
		*Quintozene containing > 1 g/kg of HCB or > 10 g/kg pentachlorobenzene

*N.B. These pesticides are not expressly banned if the stated purity requirements are satisfied.

example, this work is augmented by Mack's own routine survey work in the UK and is designed to counter both cholera and pesticide abuse scares, and confirm the operation of "best practice".

- Farmers are encouraged to minimise their use of agrochemicals and to adopt integrated crop management systems, a move strongly supported by the UK multiple retail outlets, and to re-cycle crop residues where this does not constitute a pest or disease hazard.

- It is useful to provide a Code of Practice on the use of pesticides by suppliers. For example Mack provides such a code (Anon., 1994). In addition a list of UK/EC banned or severely restricted pesticides (Anon., 1992b) and current **maximum residue levels** (MRL) for relevant crops should be provided. Suppliers should be encouraged to participate in any available training schemes for spray operators; for example, it is a requirement of Mack suppliers that spray diaries are maintained and made available for inspection during visits.

RESULTS

Such policies can only be successful when they are developed in total cooperation with overseas suppliers and perhaps by being used to reinforce GIFAP "Safe Use" initiatives (Ledru et al., this volume). The Irish cucumber incident (Anon., 1992a) has shown very clearly the commercial and legal risks if there is a lack of safeguards in this area. The Technical Director's responsibilities start before a seed is sown and only end when a consumer has been satisfied by eating the product. For example, in discharging these duties, the Mack Technical Director in 1993 made 30 visits to 15 countries spending 172 days overseas, whilst Product Managers also made many visits reinforcing the policy. It is a vindication of this system that examination of the last three years of records shows no MRL exceeded on our products from less-developed countries. Most of our results show no pesticides detected, but where they are, they fall most often around the 10% of MRL figure.

CONCLUSIONS

A rigorous approach is necessary to address successfully the requirements of the UK Food Safety Act 1990. This approach has several benefits for suppliers overseas. Firstly, it creates increased awareness of the requirements of all the leading UK multiple retail outlets, who represent nearly 70% of the UK produce market. Secondly, achieving these standards of control opens up all the other markets of Europe which will be affected by similar legislation likely to be adopted by the European Union in the near future.

A programme of continuing education, training and visits is necessary to support such an approach for the foreseeable future, as legislation on MRLs, permitted pesticides and crop clearances is only likely to become more restrictive. These changes may lead to the UK consumer needing to be educated to focus less on the cosmetic qualities of his/her fresh produce, and more on its intrinsic quality and value in a healthy diet. Above all the challenge is to supply food which is safe to eat and to avoid genuine food scares which could be attributed to imperfect or poor controls at that part of our food supply which originates in the developing world.

REFERENCES

Anon. (1991a) *Food Safety Act, 1990*, Ch.16. 3rd impression. London: HMSO.

Anon. (1991b) Food Safety and Nutrition Groups at odds over pesticide residues. *Supermarket Business* **1**, 19-22.

Anon. (1992a) *Cucumber Health Warning*. Dublin: Department of Agriculture and Food Statement, 117/92.

Anon. (1992b) *Pesticides*, Part Iv. London: Ministry of Agriculture, Fisheries and Foods/Health and Safety Executive.

Anon. (1994) *Code of Practice for Pesticide Control*. 3rd edn. London: Fresh Produce Consortium.

Legge, A.P.; Bugler, C.J. (1994) *Mack Quality Assurance Manual*. Paddock Wood, UK: Mack Multiples Division.

Ridge, S.R. (1991) Pesticides and the campaign for their reduction. *British Food Journal* **93**, 30-32.

Spriegel, G. (1993) *Sainsbury policy on the Integrated Crop Management System*. (Document circulated to all Sainsbury fresh produce suppliers).